THE WORLD OF 5G

Volume 2

INTELLIGENT MANUFACTURING

THE WORLD OF 5G
(In 5 Volumes)

5G的世界 — 万物互联
Originally published in Chinese by Guangdong Science and Technology Press Co., Ltd.
Copyright © Guangdong Science and Technology Press Co., Ltd. 2020

The World of 5G — Internet of Everything, Vol. 1
Copyright © 2022 by World Scientific Publishing Co. Pte. Ltd.

5G的世界 — 智能制造
Originally published in Chinese by Guangdong Science and Technology Press Co., Ltd.
Copyright © Guangdong Science and Technology Press Co., Ltd. 2020

The World of 5G — Intelligent Manufacturing, Vol. 2
Copyright © 2022 by World Scientific Publishing Co. Pte. Ltd.

5G的世界 — 智能家居
Originally published in Chinese by Guangdong Science and Technology Press Co., Ltd.
Copyright © Guangdong Science and Technology Press Co., Ltd. 2020

The World of 5G — Intelligent Home, Vol. 3
Copyright © 2022 by World Scientific Publishing Co. Pte. Ltd.

5G的世界 — 智慧交通
Originally published in Chinese by Guangdong Science and Technology Press Co., Ltd.
Copyright © Guangdong Science and Technology Press Co., Ltd. 2020

The World of 5G — Intelligent Transportation, Vol. 4
Copyright © 2022 by World Scientific Publishing Co. Pte. Ltd.

5G的世界 — 智慧医疗
Originally published in Chinese by Guangdong Science and Technology Press Co., Ltd.
Copyright © Guangdong Science and Technology Press Co., Ltd. 2020

The World of 5G — Intelligent Medicine, Vol. 5
Copyright © 2022 by World Scientific Publishing Co. Pte. Ltd.

THE WORLD OF 5G

Volume 2

INTELLIGENT MANUFACTURING

Jishun Guo
Joyson Intelligent Automotive Research Institute, China

Translators
Wenjia Han
Yimei (Beijing) Technology Co., Ltd
Stuart Cao
Shenzhen Skyly Words Technology Co., Ltd

Proofreader
Lianghe Dong
Mudanjiang Normal University, China

NEW JERSEY · LONDON · SINGAPORE · BEIJING · SHANGHAI · HONG KONG · TAIPEI · CHENNAI · TOKYO

Published by

World Scientific Publishing Co. Pte. Ltd.

5 Toh Tuck Link, Singapore 596224

USA office: 27 Warren Street, Suite 401-402, Hackensack, NJ 07601

UK office: 57 Shelton Street, Covent Garden, London WC2H 9HE

Library of Congress Cataloging-in-Publication Data

Names: Xue, Quan (Telecommunications professor), editor-in-chief.

Title: The world of 5G / authors, Quan Xue, South China University of Technology, China,
Wenquan Che, South China University of Technology, China, Jishun Guo,
Joyson Intelligent Automotive Research Institute, China, Wei Wu, Skyworth Group Co., Ltd., China,
Zhiqiang Xu, Guangzhou Hantele Communication Co., Ltd., China, Wenhua Huang,
Southern Medical University, China, Haibin Lin, Affiliated Hospital of Putian University, China.

Description: Singapore ; Hackensack, NJ : World Scientific Publishing Co. Pte. Ltd, [2022] |
Includes bibliographical references and index. | Contents: v. 1. Internet of everything --
v. 2. Intelligent manufacturing -- v. 3. Intelligent home -- v. 4. Intelligent transportation --
v. 5. Intelligent medicine.

Identifiers: LCCN 2021061659 | ISBN 9789811250170 (set ; hardcover) | ISBN 9789811250187
(set ; ebook for institutions) | ISBN 9789811250194 (set ; ebook for individuals) |
ISBN 9789811244131 (v. 1 ; hardcover) | ISBN 9789811244148 (v. 1 ; ebook for institutions) |
ISBN 9789811244155 (v. 1 ; ebook for individuals) | ISBN 9789811244223 (v. 2 ; hardcover) |
ISBN 9789811244230 (v. 2 ; ebook for institutions) | ISBN 9789811244247 (v. 2 ; ebook for individuals) |
ISBN 9789811244254 (v. 3 ; hardcover) | ISBN 9789811244261 (v. 3 ; ebook for institutions) |
ISBN 9789811244278 (v. 3 ; ebook for individuals) | ISBN 9789811244162 (v. 4 ; hardcover) |
ISBN 9789811244179 (v. 4 ; ebook for institutions | ISBN 9789811244186 (v. 4 ; ebook for individuals) |
ISBN 9789811244193 (v. 5 ; hardcover) | ISBN 9789811244209 (v. 5 ; ebook for institutions) |
ISBN 9789811244216 (v. 5 ; ebook for individuals)

Subjects: LCSH: 5G mobile communication systems. | Expert systems (Computer science) | Automation.

Classification: LCC TK5103.25 .X84 2022 | DDC 621.3845/6--dc23/eng/20220224

LC record available at https://lccn.loc.gov/2021061659

British Library Cataloguing-in-Publication Data

A catalogue record for this book is available from the British Library.

Copyright © 2022 by World Scientific Publishing Co. Pte. Ltd.

All rights reserved. This book, or parts thereof, may not be reproduced in any form or by any means, electronic or mechanical, including photocopying, recording or any information storage and retrieval system now known or to be invented, without written permission from the publisher.

For photocopying of material in this volume, please pay a copying fee through the Copyright Clearance Center, Inc., 222 Rosewood Drive, Danvers, MA 01923, USA. In this case permission to photocopy is not required from the publisher.

For any available supplementary material, please visit
https://www.worldscientific.com/worldscibooks/10.1142/12479#t=suppl

Printed in Singapore

Foreword
5G Empowers the Society for
Development at a Rapid Speed

Being one of the buzzwords of the global media in recent years, 5G is very attractive because it carries great expectations from people, both in terms of the communication technology itself and the industry changes it could unleash. Recalling the development of human society, technological change is undoubtedly one of the biggest engines. Marked by the invention of the steam engine and electricity, the first two Industrial Revolutions featured mechanization and electrification, respectively. As the wheel of history rolls into the 21st century, a new round of Industrial Revolution featuring intelligence will be looming, and its impact on human civilization and economic development will be no less than that of the previous two Industrial Revolutions. But then what is pushing it? Compared with the previous two, the new Industrial Revolution is no longer pushed by a single technology but instead by the integration of multiple technologies, among which mobile communication, Internet, artificial intelligence, and biotechnology are the decisive elements.

5G, as the commanding heights of modern mobile technology, is an important engine that enables other key technologies mentioned above. Meanwhile, it can also be seen that 5G comes out when the new momentum is needed most by the Internet development. After almost linear rapid growth, the increment rate of China's Internet users is falling with the popularity rate of mobile phones almost refusing to grow. Owning to the fast pace of life, the netizens now pursue new forms of business with short periods, low investments, and quick returns. Faster speed and lower fees have mitigated the cost pressure on broadband Internet access when short videos and small programs are becoming popular. But these are still not enough to meet the requirements of the new format of the Internet. The future development of the Internet calls for new drivers and new models to solve this problem. The industrial Internet, regarded as the second half of the Internet, has just started, and its new driving forces cannot fill deficiencies of the consumer Internet driving force. At present, the Internet enters into a transition period of continuity for new drivers to replace the old ones. At a time when the consumption of the Internet needs to be intensified and the industrial Internet is starting to take off, 5G comes into being.

As the latest generation of cellular mobile communication technology, 5G is characterized by high speed, low latency, wide connectivity, and high reliability. Compared with 4G, 5G's peak rate increases by 30 times, user experience rate advances by 10 times, and spectrum efficiency accelerates by three times. Moreover, compared to 4G, 5G mobile supports high-speed rail with the speed of 500 km/h, with its wireless interface delay reduced by 90%, the connection density enhanced by 10 times, energy efficiency and traffic density improved by 100 times, enough to support the mobile Internet industry and many applications of the Internet. Compared with the previous four generations of mobile communication technologies, the most important change in 5G is the shift from individual-oriented use to industry-oriented applications, providing indispensable high-speed, massive, and low-latency connectivity for Internet of Everything needed by the new round of Industrial Revolution. Therefore, 5G is not only merely a communication technology but also an important "infrastructure".

It is well timed and also quite accountable in cultural inheritance for Guangdong Science and Technology Publishing House to take the lead in organizing the compilation and distribution of this book series and to popularize 5G knowledge in the society for improving the national scientific literacy when the whole society is talking about 5G with great expectations. Compared with the numerous books about 5G in the market, this series stands out with its own characteristics. First of all, Professor Xue Quan, the Chief Editor, who has been focusing on the research of 5G cutting-edge core technologies in recent years, is an expert in the fields of millimeter wave and terahertz. He took the lead in the compilation of this series with his team responsible for the volume, *5G Internet of Everything*, thus aiming to well leverage the tool for the popularization of science to present 5G technology mass-orientally. In addition, with the focus on the integration and application of 5G in the vertical industry, the series comes out just in line with the close social concerns about 5G. The team included industry experts from the Guangdong Provincial Key Laboratory of Millimeter Wave and Terahertz in the South China University of Technology, Automotive Engineering Research Institute of Guangzhou Automobile Group Co., Ltd., Southern Medical University, Guangzhou Hanxin Communication Technology Co., Ltd., Skyworth Group Co., Ltd., for the corresponding volume, respectively. This book series is targeted at the current pain points of the industry, yet contributes to an unfettered imagination of the future of the 5G-enabling industry. It will be an invaluable science book for the public yearning for new technology for a new round of industrial transformation. The first issue of the book series consists of five volumes.

What's remarkable is that while the book focuses on how 5G will revolutionize the vertical industry if integrated with other technologies, it also explores the possible negative effects of technological advances on human beings. In the progress of science and technology, it is essential to stick to human nature, ethics, morality, and law. So the acceleration of the development of science and technology, with "safety valve" and "brake" being indispensable, shouldn't be based on the sacrifice of the dominance of human nature and the thinking ability of human beings. We need to think of science and technology as a "double-edged sword" and better exploit the advantages and avoid disadvantages while turning the passive reaction into an active response.

Coming in with a roar, 5G will have an immeasurable impact on the development of human society. Let's work together and march toward the future.

Wu Hequan
Member of Chinese Academy of Engineering

Foreword
5G as the Engine for Upgrading and Development of the Vertical Industries

As we all know, we are gradually entering a digital era, and many industries and technologies will progress around the data chain, in which the main effect of mobile communication technology is data transmission. Applications that require performance such as high-definition video, multi-device access, and real-time two-way interaction between multiple people are difficult to achieve without the support of high-speed communication technology. As the latest generation of cellular mobile communication technology, 5G features high speed, low delay, wide connection, and high reliability.

The year 2020 marks the first year for 5G commercial use and then the employment of 5G is expected to peak around 2035. 5G will be mainly applied in the following seven fields: smart creation, smart city, smart grid, smart office, smart security, telemedicine and health care, and commercial retail. In these seven fields, it is estimated that nearly 50% of 5G components will be applied to smart creation, while nearly 18.7% will be applied to smart city construction.

The importance of 5G is not only reflected in its great promotion of upgrading industries such as smart creation but also reflected in its direct correlation with the development of artificial intelligence. The development of artificial intelligence requires a large number of user cases and data, and the amount of data that 4G Internet of Things (IoT) can provide for learning is incomparable to that of 5G. Therefore, the development of

x *The World of 5G: Intelligent Manufacturing*

5G IoT plays a very important role in promoting the development of artificial intelligence. Relying on 5G can help promote the upgrading of many vertical industries. It is also for this reason that 5G's leading development has become an important engine to promote the development of national science and technology and economy and has also become the focus of competition between China and the United States in the field of science and technology.

Against this background, Guangdong Science and Technology Publishing House took the lead in organizing the compilation and distribution of the "5G World" book series, with the focus on the integrated application and empowerment of 5G in many industries, including manufacturing, medical care, transportation, home furniture, finance, education, and so on. On the one hand, it is a courageous and culturally responsible measure to popularize 5G among the public, enhancing national scientific literacy. On the other hand, this book is also an utterly precious reference for industry insiders who want to understand the trend for the development of 5G technology and industrial integration.

This book series was done under the guidance of Chief Editor, Professor Xue Quan, the Director of the Guangdong Key Laboratory of Millimeter Wave and Terahertz, South China University of Technology. As an expert in the fields of millimeter wave and terahertz technology, Professor Xue Quan will manage to make a book series of popular science with accurate and natural technical features. This book series is scheduled to be publish the first editions of five volumes, including *The World of 5G: Internet of Everything, The World of 5G: Intelligent Manufacturing, The World of 5G: Intelligent Home, The World of 5G: Intelligent Transportation,* and *The World of 5G: Intelligent Medicine.* The compilation team of this series boasts of strong support. In addition to *The World of 5G: Internet of Everything*, which was written by the technical team of Guangdong Millimeter Wave and Terahertz Key Laboratory of South China University of Technology, the other four volumes were mainly written by relevant industry experts. Among all the volumes, *The World of 5G: Intelligent Manufacturing* was written by experts from the Auto Engineering Research Institute of Guangzhou Automobile Group Co., Ltd., while *The World of 5G: Intelligent Medicine* was written by experts from Southern Medical University. *The World of 5G: Intelligent Transportation* was written by Guangzhou Hantele Communication Co., Ltd., and *The World of 5G: Intelligent Home* was written by Skyworth Group Co., Ltd. This kind of cross-industry combination writing team possesses a strong complementary and professional system for the following reasons: for one thing, technical experts can fully grasp the evolution of mobile communication technology and key technologies of 5G; for another, industry experts can accurately feel the pain points of the industry as well as analyze the advantages and challenges of the industries integrated with 5G through incise writing around the central themes to provide a valuable reference for industry peers with real and vivid cases.

Besides a vivid description of the huge changes that could be brought about by the 5G technology merged into industries, what makes this book novel and fresh is the fact that they also discuss the negative effects the rapid advance of technology may have on human beings. The rapid development of high technology should not be done at the cost of human nature, ethics, and thoughts. It is necessary to make sure that technology conforms to science and ethics with the essential "cushion" and "safety valve".

Mao Junfa
Member of Chinese Academy of Sciences

Preface

As a revolutionary leap in technology, 5G provides Internet of Everything with important technical support. Furthermore, it will bring prosperity for mobile Internet and industrial Internet and provide many industries with unprecedented opportunities, thus being expected to trigger profound changes in the whole society. What is 5G? How will 5G empower various industries and promote a new round of Industrial Revolution? The answers can be found in the series *The World of 5G*, which consists of five volumes.

The volume *The World of 5G: Internet of Everything* is edited by Xue Quan, Director of Guangdong Key Laboratory of Millimeter Wave and Terahertz, South China University of Technology, and mainly expounds the iterative development history of mobile communication technology, the characteristics and limitations of the first four generations of mobile communication technology, the technical characteristics of 5G and its possible industrial application prospects, and the development trend of mobile communication technology in the post-5G era. By reading this volume, the reader can obtain a carefully and skillfully drawn picture of the past, present, and future applications of 5G.

The volume *The World of 5G: Intelligent Manufacturing* is edited by Dr. Guo Jishun of Automotive Engineering Research Institute of Guangzhou Automobile Group Co., Ltd., and mainly introduces the development process of the Industrial Revolution, the opportunity brought about by 5G to the manufacturing industry, the upgrade of smart creation assisted by 5G, and the application of intelligent production based on 5G. Through this volume, readers can understand the opportunities for the transformation of traditional manufacturing produced by 5G+ smart creation and learn by experience what kind of revolution manufacturing innovation will create in the society.

The volume *The World of 5G: Intelligent Home* is edited by Wu Wei from Skyworth Group Co., Ltd., and mainly elaborates on the evolution of smart home, the key technologies that 5G uses to facilitate the intelligent development of home life, as well as innovative smart home products based on 5G technology. Home furnishing is closely tied to our daily life. By reading this volume, readers can understand the convenience and comfort arising from the integration of 5G and smart home. It provides a glimpse of the wonderful life that technology has created.

The volume *The World of 5G: Intelligent Transportation* is edited by Xu Zhiqiang from Guangzhou Hexin Communications Technology Co., Ltd., and mainly describes the development process of smart transportation, the key 5G technologies and architectures used in smart transportation, as well as the application examples of smart transportation based on 5G. By reading this volume, readers can be fully informed about the future development trend of smart transportation led by 5G technology.

The volume *The Word of 5G: Intelligent Medicine* is edited by Huang Wenhua and Lin Haibin from Southern Medical University, and mainly focuses on the effect of the integration of 5G and medical treatment, including the advantages of smart medicine compared with traditional medical treatment, how 5G promotes the development of smart medicine and smart medicine terminals and new medical applications integrated with 5G. Reading between the lines, readers can gain a comprehensive understanding of the huge application potential of 5G technology in the medical industry and be keenly aware of the well-being that technological progress has contributed to human health.

Finally, we specially acknowledge the funding from projects such as prior research and development projects "Key Technology of Millimeter Wave Integrated RF Front-end System Compatible with C Band (2018YFB1802000)" of the National Ministry of Science and Technology, the major science and technology project of "Research on 5G Millimeter Wave Broadband High Efficiency Chip and Phased Array System (2018B010115001)" of Guangdong Science and Technology Department, and Strategic Consulting Project of "Guangdong New Generation Information Technology Development Strategy Research (201816611292)" of Guangdong Research Institute of Chinese Academy of Engineering Development Strategy.

5G brings us technological change, industry upgrade, and social upheaval with unprecedented speed and strength, while also generating great challenges. Let's navigate our way ahead while harnessing the waves of 5G.

About the Author

Jishun Guo, Ph.D. in Artificial Intelligence and Robotics, is currently the leader of Intelligent Driving Technology Department of the GAC R&D Center and the Technical Director of L3/L4 autopilot of the GAC group. He has completed undergraduate, Master's and doctoral degrees at the University of Electronic Science and Technology, National Tsing Hua University, Swiss Federal Institute of Technology Zurich, and Stanford University.

Before coming to the GAC R&D Center, Dr. Guo, the Recruitment high-level expert of Guangzhou in 2017, worked on artificial intelligence technology development at Google X-lab, EMC China Research Institute and Institute of Deep Learning. He has won the Asian Gold Medal in the ACM Algorithm Competition, the International Scholar Award in the Ministry of Education, Culture, Sports, Science and Technology, the Erasmus Mundus Full Scholarship, and the Outstanding Scholar Awards on both sides of the Taiwan Straits. He has presided over and participated in the 973 National Key Basic Research Project, the National Major Basic Research Project, and the New Century Excellent Talents Project of the Ministry of Education. Dr. Guo has published more than 20 papers in core journals and conferences at home and abroad, and applied for 28 invention patents in Chinese and American.

Contents

Foreword: 5G Empowers the Society for Development at a Rapid Speed   v

Foreword: 5G as the Engine for Upgrading and Development of the Vertical Industries   ix

Preface   xiii

About the Author   xvii

Chapter 1 The Call of the Times: Opportunities and Challenges of the Fourth Industrial Revolution   **1**

1.1 The First Three Industrial Revolutions   1

     1.1.1 The first industrial revolution   1

     1.1.2 The second industrial revolution   2

     1.1.3 The third industrial revolution   3

1.2 The Beginning of the Fourth Industrial Revolution   4

     1.2.1 Germany's "Industry 4.0"   5

     1.2.2 America's "National networking of manufacturing innovation"   6

     1.2.3 Japan's "Industrial value chain initiative"   8

1.3 Opportunities and Challenges   10

Chapter 2 Brave Winds and Waves: Smart Manufacturing is the Key to Leading the Fourth Industrial Revolution   **13**

2.1 The Meaning of Intelligent Manufacturing   15

xx *The World of 5G: Intelligent Manufacturing*

2.2	How Intelligent Is Intelligent Manufacturing?	19
	2.2.1 The characteristics of intelligent manufacturing	19
	2.2.2 The performance of intelligent manufacturing	23
2.3	How to Achieve Intelligent Manufacturing	27
2.4	The Demand of Intelligent Manufacturing for New Networks	32

Chapter 3 5G Upgrade of Intelligent Manufacturing: A Major Opportunity for Industrial Upgrading   **35**

3.1	5G+ The Overall Architecture of Intelligent Manufacturing	36
	3.1.1 Data layer	38
	3.1.2 Network layer	38
	3.1.3 Platform layer	39
	3.1.4 Application layer	39
3.2	5G+ Key Technologies of Intelligent Manufacturing	40
	3.2.1 5G TSN (time-sensitive networking) technology	40
	3.2.2 Network slicing technology	40
	3.2.3 Mobile edge computing (MEC) technology	41
	3.2.4 Industrial cloud platform technology	42
	3.2.5 5G network security technology	43
3.3	5G+ Examples of Intelligent Manufacturing Exploration	44
	3.3.1 Examples of South Korea's exploration	44
	3.3.2 Examples of China's exploration	45

Chapter 4 The Application of Intelligent Mass Production Based on 5G: Overcoming the Obstacles of Intelligent Production   **47**

4.1	Application of Information Physical System Based on 5G	47
	4.1.1 The access of massive number of sensors to factories	48
	4.1.2 Industrial cloud platform	54
	4.1.3 Industrial digital transformation	62
4.2	5G-Driven Industrial AR/VR Applications	69
	4.2.1 Super flexible deployment and upgrade of AR/VR-assisted intelligent manufacturing	69
	4.2.2 Definition and overview of virtual reality	70
	4.2.3 Industrial wearables and flexible deployment of industrial image processing	72
	4.2.4 Automatic transmission and data acquisition of factory information	73

4.2.5 Artificial takeover of intelligent assembly and industrial robots	78
4.2.6 Expert business support and remote maintenance	79
4.2.7 Skilled inheritance system based on artificial intelligence teaching and virtualization training	82
4.3 Industry Robot Backed by 5G Cloud	87
4.3.1 Cooperation of multiple flexible robots	91
4.3.2 Industrial control robot formation with low time delay and precision synchronization	94
4.3.3 The optimization, mining and sharing mode of production skills based on Big Data cloud platform	96
4.4 Customized Production of the Whole Life Cycle of Products Supported by 5G	98
4.4.1 Online customer customization system based on 5G AR-Cloud	99
4.4.2 Aided design of intelligent products based on Big Data + IoT	102
4.4.3 Small-scale customized production based on ultra-flexible manufacturing	104
4.5 5G Facilitates Intelligent Resource Allocation	109
4.5.1 5G helps intelligent warehouse management	109
4.5.2 5G will boost intelligent logistics supply	110
4.6 5G Helps Optimize the Upstream and Downstream Design of the Supply Chain	115
4.6.1 Collaborative optimization design of upstream and downstream data of the supply chain based on 5G	115
4.6.2 Typical application of 5G+ collaborative optimization design — semiconductor equipment	116
Conclusion	119
Bibliography	123
Index	125

Chapter 1

The Call of the Times: Opportunities and Challenges of the Fourth Industrial Revolution

1.1 The First Three Industrial Revolutions

Beginning in Britain in the 1760s, the Industrial Revolution had a profound impact on the British society and brought about changes in their production mode, lifestyle, as well as the modes of the enterprises' operations and management. Enterprises' organizational forms have changed from the manufactory and factory system in the First Industrial Revolution, bureaucracy in the Second Industrial Revolution to the shareholding system in the Third Industrial Revolution. A number of management methods have emerged during the process, and enterprises in each period were optimized by every Industrial Revolution.

1.1.1 *The first industrial revolution*

Beginning in the 1760s and ending in the mid-19th century, according to most scholars, the First Industrial Revolution was marked by the invention and application of the steam engine (Fig. 1.1). During the last few decades, Britain has witnessed the advent of a series of technological inventions that led the human society from the era of manpower to a time of machines. These inventions changed the production methods of Britain's cotton textile industry before quickly expanding

Figure 1.1 The First Industrial Revolution.

to the wool textile industry and other industries, ushering in the world's industrialization.

Following were the key features of the First Industrial Revolution: (1) the organization model of a manufactory with the relative importance of industrial input factors shifted from labor force to capital; (2) manual labor is replaced by machine production and manufactories by the factory system; (3) enterprises are more interconnected and the original industrial structure is dominated by the secondary industry instead of the primary industry; (4) the process of urbanization started.

It should be noted that during the First Industrial Revolution, the inventors of new machines in the textile and other industries were mainly skilled workers with rich experience but limited scientific knowledge, which significantly hindered the later industrialization stage in Britain.

1.1.2 *The second industrial revolution*

The Second Industrial Revolution (Fig. 1.2), featuring the wide application of internal combustion engines, electricity, and petroleum, started in the 1850s and ended in the early 20th century. The Second Industrial Revolution witnessed a large number of impressive inventions, as represented by the disc dynamo, the first generator in human history invented by Michael Faraday ("the Father of Electricity" and "the

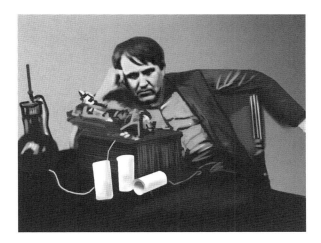

Figure 1.2 The Second Industrial Revolution.

Father of Alternating Current") in 1831 upon his discovery of the electromagnetism induction phenomenon, which replaced the steam engines used in factories. The application of the new inventions and technologies in factories presented a heavy blow to the original industrial system, which was thus gradually reshaped and mankind entered the era of electrification.

Following were the key features of the Second Industrial Revolution: (1) a remarkable increase in industrial labor productivity; (2) an upgrade in the organization and management model as well as production mode within the enterprise; (3) more concentrated industrial organization; (4) the heavy chemical industry as a driving force for a nation's overall growth.

1.1.3 *The third industrial revolution*

The Third Industrial Revolution, driven by the development of computer and semiconductor technology, began in the 1940s and the 1950s and ended in the 1990s. Compared with the previous two Industrial Revolutions, the Third Industrial Revolution no longer relies on electricity, aircraft manufacturing, petroleum, chemical engineering, and other industries. Moreover, labor force and capital no longer served as the most important inputs in production. The industrial transformation and economic growth found their source in the products and technologies based on silicon, which contributed to automation in the Third Industrial Revolution from mechanization in the First Industrial Revolution and electrification in the Second Industrial Revolution.

Following were the key features of the Third Industrial Revolution: (1) integration of information technologies; (2) apparent changes in the enterprises' production, management, and forms of organization; (3) a more "softened" and advanced industrial structure.

1.2 The Beginning of the Fourth Industrial Revolution

With the popularization of global IT applications, scientific and technological innovation clusters in multiple fields, including the Internet, cloud computing, quantum technology, artificial intelligence, Big Data, and biological sciences, started to emerge in large numbers globally since the 1990s. As shown in Fig. 1.3, the Fourth Industrial Revolution featuring intelligence is approaching, facilitating technological revolution and industrial transformation and bringing both opportunities and challenges to the development of different industries in countries around the world. Countries started to develop intelligent manufacturing by proposing respective countermeasures, such as "Industry 4.0" in Germany, "National Network for Manufacturing Innovation (NNMI)" in America, and "Industrial Value Chain Initiative" in Japan.

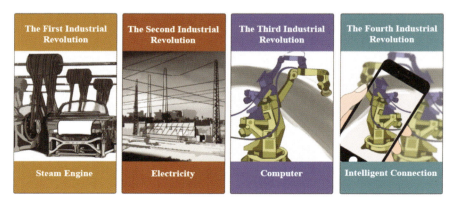

Figure 1.3   The evolvement of the Four Industrial Revolutions.

1.2.1 *Germany's "Industry 4.0"*

Since the 1970s, computers and information technology have become the core technologies of the Third Industrial Revolution. In developed countries, more than 90% of industrial manufacturing is dependent on computers and information technology, which has brought fundamental changes to human life, work, and study. At the Hannover Messe in 2013, the German government formally proposed "Industry 4.0" and declared it as the Fourth Industrial Revolution led by intelligent manufacturing. Jointly funded by the Federal Ministry of Education and Research and the Federal Ministry for Economic Affairs and Energy, the project has been upgraded to a national strategy with €200 million investment by the German government under the advice and help of German academic and industrial communities, such as acatech, the Fraunhofer Society, and Siemens. The essential prerequisite for "Industry 4.0" is the automation of industries and improvement of manufacturing intelligence, especially in the fields of electrical engineering and machine manufacturing. The reference architecture of Germany's "Industry 4.0" is shown in Fig. 1.4.

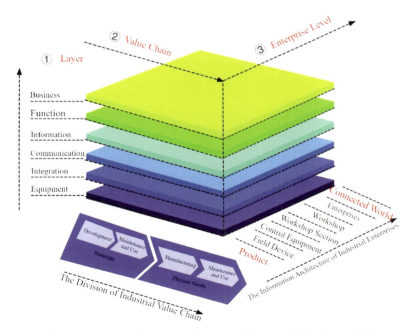

Figure 1.4 The reference architecture of Germany's "Industry 4.0".

6   *The World of 5G: Intelligent Manufacturing*

Based on the cyber-physical system (CPS), the core of "Industry 4.0" is to realize the four intelligent transformations, namely, intelligent factories, intelligent production, intelligent logistics, and intelligent products. These can be described as follows: (1) intelligent factory mainly studies the realization of intelligent production systems and processes as well as networked, distributed production facilities; (2) intelligent production mainly involves logistics management, man–machine interaction, and the application of 3D printing technology in enterprises' production processes; (3) intelligent logistics, which mainly integrates all the logistics information, closely connects the demand side and the supply side of logistics resources and quickly matches logistics information through the Internet of Things (IoT) and Internet; (4) intelligent products, which are mainly industrial products made during the new Industrial Revolution, boast of intelligent manufacturing based on integrated value networks, intelligent factories supporting the IoT, and Internet of services as well as the entire production process of the intelligent production line.

1.2.2 *America's "National networking of manufacturing innovation"*

In the early 21st century, multinational companies kept cropping up in the United States, along with a massive outflow of domestic manufacturing industries, resulting in "industry hollowing". In 2008, heavy dependence on the virtual economy (such as finance and service industries) led to a financial crisis in the States, which then spread globally. Around 2010, the added value of China's manufacturing industry surpassed that of the United States, whose status in the manufacturing industry declined worldwide. After the financial crisis, upon the reflection over the negative impact of the virtual economy, the United States undertook to revitalize the real economy based upon a series of plans rolled out for the real economy, such as A *Framework for Revitalizing American Manufacturing* issued in December 2009 to advance the manufacturing industry through financial support and investment guidance.

In 2011, the United States President's Council of Advisors on Science and Technology put forward the *Strategy on Ensuring American Leadership in Advanced Manufacturing*, which accelerated the introduction of *Advanced Manufacturing Partnership* and *Revitalize American Manufacturing and Innovation Act*. In 2012, US President Barack Obama proposed to build "National Networking of Manufacturing Innovation", established an innovation pilot institution, and invested $1 billion in 2013. In 2014, the idea of "National Networking of Manufacturing Innovation" was put forward and recognized after passing a bill, before it was renamed as "Manufacturing USA" in 2016. The above process can be roughly summarized into the following three stages: reducing manufacturing costs, building the National Networking of Manufacturing Innovation, and reshaping American manufacturing.

The American government promoted the development of the manufacturing industry by encouraging technological innovation and easing policies, attaching importance to talent training and strategies such as attracting high-tech talents and promoting export in an effort to bring back overseas manufacturers that previously outflowed from America and strengthen their dominant position in the manufacturing industry. Under the guidance of various policies, the added value of the US manufacturing industry kept rising year by year since 2009 and reached the highest level prior to the 2007 financial crisis by 2016, as shown in Fig. 1.5. "National Networking of Manufacturing Innovation" focuses on improving the innovation capabilities of the manufacturing industry, whereas "Manufacturing USA" emphasizes the productization and commercialization of innovation. Under the "Manufacturing USA" policy, the year 2017 saw the establishment of six new innovation agencies and a total of 14 intelligent innovation institutes in the United States. The share of federal funds

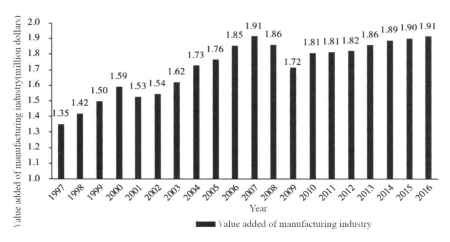

Figure 1.5 Changes in the added value of the manufacturing industry in America over time.

8   *The World of 5G: Intelligent Manufacturing*

earmarked for R&D projects continued to increase, with the ratio of federal funds to non-federal funds reaching 1.5:1 from the previously set 1:1. Supported by project funds, the total number of R&D projects also increased, with a more than 50% increase in the total member count in the innovation system.

1.2.3 *Japan's "Industrial Value Chain Initiative"*

Since the Second World War, Japan has gradually become a global leader in automotive electronics, microelectronics, and precision instruments. Japan's intelligent manufacturing started around the 1990s. In 1990, Japan made a 10-year development plan, ushering in the era of "intelligence" for its manufacturing industry. In 1995, Japan put forward the strategy of "building the country through scientific and technological innovation", offering policy support for intelligent production. Ever since the 21st century, Japan's *Basic Plan for Science and Technology* centers on developing emerging industries, such as information technology, nanotechnology, and biotechnology. Since 2015, Japan has rolled out a series of measures for the advancement of intelligent manufacturing, including new strategies for robotics, industrial value chain plans, interconnected industrial strategies, white papers of the manufacturing industry, and a comprehensive strategy for scientific and technological innovation. Morgan Stanley released in 2018 that from 2018 to 2020, the expenditure on intelligent manufacturing by large Japanese companies rose from 10.6% to 22.8%.

Japan's Industrial Value Chain Initiative was initiated by the Japan Society of Mechanical Engineers. A cooperation system that integrates the "government, industry, universities and research institutes" has been established. This plan was originally designed to solve the recurring problems in the technology development and save manpower, material resources, costs, and time for small- and medium-sized enterprises in smart manufacturing. In December 2016, Japan's Industrial Value Chain Initiative (IVI) released *The Reference Architecture of Industrial Value Chain*. It can be seen from Fig. 1.6 that the three dimensions of the intelligent manufacturing units are asset view, management view, and activity view. In the general function blocks of intelligent manufacturing, intelligent manufacturing units can be combined in various ways according to different levels to present the industrial chain in an all-round way from multiple perspectives (Fig. 1.7) and establish an interconnection mode between different intelligent factories. The reference architecture of the

The Call of the Times 9

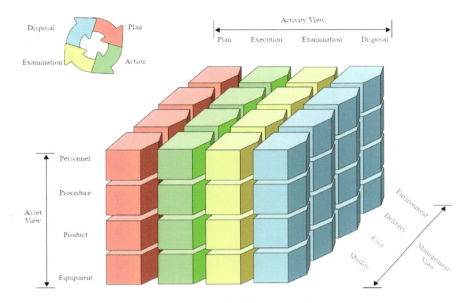

Figure 1.6 3D model of intelligent manufacturing units.

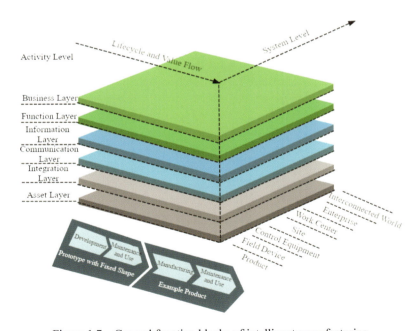

Figure 1.7 General function blocks of intelligent manufacturing.

10 *The World of 5G: Intelligent Manufacturing*

industrial manufacturing chain provides strong theoretical support for the implementation of intelligent manufacturing strategies and demonstrates Japan's powerful advantages in smart manufacturing. In March 2018, the Industrial Value Chain Initiative introduced a new generation of reference architecture of the industrial value chain with further optimization and substantially increased practicality.

1.3 Opportunities and Challenges

Since the founding of the People's Republic of China, China's manufacturing industry has turned from "learning from the Soviet Union's industrial system", "reform and opening up, and original equipment manufacturing", to "the rise of Chinese manufacturing". In the 1980s, "homegrown products" were found in thousands of Chinese households. As a latecomer to the Third Industrial Revolution, China finished the Third Industrial Revolution within just over 20 years. In the 1990s, manufacturing policy easing enabled China's transition from a planned economy to a market economy. From 1978 to 1998, China's manufacturing accounted for 6% of the world's total. Since the beginning of the 21st century, China's manufacturing industry has experienced a massive expansion. As of 2007, China's manufacturing industry made up 13% of the world's total, second only to the United States.

China's manufacturing industry was in trouble amid rapid development. China lacked core independent technologies, particularly high-end dedicated chips, as 95% of the chips in computers and servers were imported. Since 2008, China's manufacturing industry has paid more attention to technological innovation. In the meantime, a large number of outstanding companies, such as Huawei, Midea, Xiaomi, DJI, and Gree, made their appearances.

Now, the Fourth Industrial Revolution is moving China forward on a path of intelligence, and "intelligent manufacturing" has become a high ground for countries' industrial development. To build an internationally competitive manufacturing industry, upgrade, and transform the traditional manufacturing industry and learn more from the foreign experience, China and Germany signed *The Joint Program of Action on Cooperation: Shaping Innovation Together* in 2014 to promote cooperation between the two countries in the fields of mobile Internet, IoT, cloud computing, Big Data, etc.

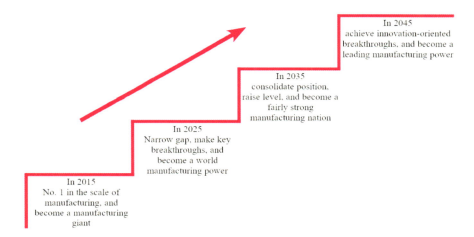

Figure 1.8 The stages of *Made in China* 2025.

China drew lessons from Germany's "Industry 4.0" and drew up an action plan for intelligent manufacturing or *Made in China* 2025 issued by the State Council in 2015. The pilot work already started in some regions. *Made in China* 2025 involves the following three stages of building a world manufacturing power: by 2025, the overall quality of the manufacturing industry will be significantly improved, with a remarkable enhancement in the innovation capability and labor productivity and further integration of industrialization and IT application; by 2035, China will be a fairly strong manufacturing nation among the world manufacturing powers; by 2045, China will consolidate its position as a manufacturing power, with comprehensive strength ranking among the top of all world manufacturing powers, as shown in Fig. 1.8.

Chapter 2

Brave Winds and Waves: Smart Manufacturing is the Key to Leading the Fourth Industrial Revolution

Intelligent manufacturing, as the name implies, refers to the intelligent production activities of the manufacturing industry. It is the combination of high and new technology represented by Internet technology and the manufacturing industry and is the core of the Fourth Industrial Revolution. Since the First Industrial Revolution, the manufacturing industry has been one of the industries closely related to human activities. It belongs to a core classification of the industry, and its task is to convert manufacturing resources into tools, industrial products, and consumer products for people to use according to market requirements. In the path of human development, the "chemical reaction" between scientific and technological progress and the manufacturing industry has happened frequently, constantly giving birth to more advanced and more efficient production technology and putting more and better products in front of people. At the same time, the development of science and technology is also constantly enriching the production and management mode of the manufacturing industry, so this time-honored industry continues to break out with new vitality and positively impact the future.

As shown in Fig. 2.1, looking back at the three stages of industrial development, all leaps in manufacturing production and management level have the shadow of scientific and technological progress. In the First Industrial Revolution, the technological progress represented by the

14 *The World of 5G: Intelligent Manufacturing*

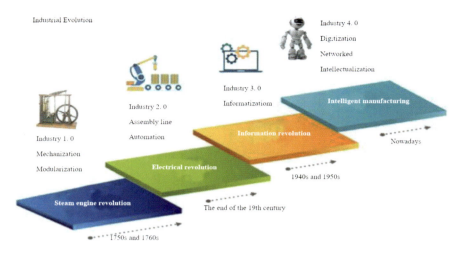

Figure 2.1   Manufacturing changes brought about by the Industrial Revolution process.

steam engine gave birth to the mechanical production and workshop management enterprises, namely the rudiment of the manufacturing industry. The Second Industrial Revolution brought about a leap in the mass production of production lines to the manufacturing industry. In addition, the establishment of the scientific management theory promoted the detailed division of labor in manufacturing technology and the functional decomposition of the manufacturing system, forming a standardized and process-based management mode with scientific management as the core. In the Third Industrial Revolution, the wide application of electronic and information technology further improved the degree of automatic control of the manufacturing process. Machines not only further took over human physical labor but also gradually began to try to take over human mental labor. Since the beginning of the 21st century, we have entered an era of intelligence. A large number of high-tech technologies, such as the Internet, Big Data, cloud computing, and the IoT, have been vigorously developed. These new technologies will be deeply integrated with all links of the manufacturing process, again bringing a new direction of upgrade to the manufacturing industry, that is, intelligent manufacturing.

But what exactly does intelligent manufacturing mean? What thorny problems does it solve? And what role will 5G play in that? This chapter attempts to shed light on these issues.

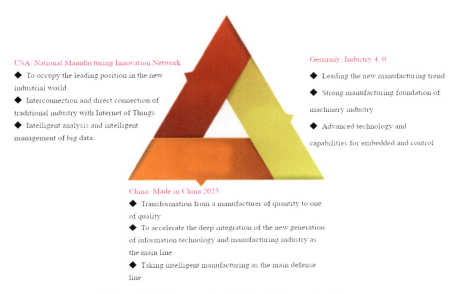

Figure 2.2   Three national industrial upgrade plans.

2.1 The Meaning of Intelligent Manufacturing

In recent years, important national industrial upgrade plans (Fig. 2.2), including China's "Made in China 2025", the "National Network for Manufacturing Innovation" of the United States, and Germany's "Industry 4.0", all regard manufacturing as the key object of upgrading. The definition of intelligent manufacturing can be found in the *Implementation Plan of 2015 Smart Manufacturing Pilot Demonstration Special Action* published by the Ministry of Industry and Information Technology of China: "Based on the new generation of information technology, the general term for advanced manufacturing processes, systems, and models which run through all links of manufacturing activities such as design, production, management and service, and has the functions of self-perception of information depth, intelligent optimization and self-decision, precise control and self-execution". The American Institute of Intelligent Manufacturing Innovation defines intelligent manufacturing as follows: "intelligent manufacturing is a combination of advanced sensing, instrumentation, monitoring, control and process optimization technologies and practices". They integrate information and communication technology with the

16   *The World of 5G: Intelligent Manufacturing*

manufacturing environment to achieve real-time management of energy, productivity, and cost in factories and enterprises.

From the introduction of intelligent manufacturing by relevant research departments, the content of intelligent manufacturing will involve the comprehensive application of the current new generation of information technology in the manufacturing industry, including sensing technology, testing technology, information technology, numerical control technology, database technology, data acquisition and processing technology, Internet technology, artificial intelligence technology, etc., to comprehensively upgrade the traditional manufacturing process, system, and model, and the upgrade will appear in the form of an intelligent factory as a whole.

The reason why the integration of this high-tech information technology and each link of the manufacturing process is called "the upgrading of the traditional manufacturing industry" is that the traditional manufacturing industry is facing new needs of the times (such as differentiated and personalized production, global response speed, environmental protection, and further improvement of energy efficiency) where the problems appear to be complex. Solving these new problems will require the manufacturing industry to come up with new ideas rather than just simple upgrades of traditional core elements.

The traditional manufacturing industry has five core elements. In the past three industrial revolutions, the key to meet the new needs of the times is often to upgrade technologies around the following five elements:

(1) *Material*: This includes characteristics and functions.
(2) *Machine*: This includes accuracy, automation, and production capacity.
(3) *Methods*: This includes process, efficiency, and productivity.
(4) *Measurement*: This includes sensor monitoring and other similar ones.
(5) *Maintenance*: This includes utilization rate, failure rate, operation and maintenance costs.

These elements are a good summary of all the key work sections of the traditional manufacturing industry. Traditional improvements and upgrades to these elements revolve around the iterated experience of professionals. No matter how much progress science and technology bring to production technology, system, and mode, the operating logic of improvement is always: Finding problems → Analyzing problems with the help of existing experience → Adjusting the five elements according to the conclusions of analysis → Solving problems → Accumulating new experiences.

In this adjustment mode, problems in the production process can be solved, and new production experience can be obtained constantly. This mode has well adapted to the development needs of the times in the past, but it is not able to adapt to the new production mode now. As markets and production are now globalized to an unprecedented extent, manufacturing needs to respond quickly to market globalization if it is to remain competitive in this environment. In addition, with the intensification of competition in the current consumer market, it has become an important trend to achieve differentiation and customized production according to consumer demand. All these require manufacturing enterprises to maintain a high degree of sensitivity and make flexible adjustments to production at any time. Since the 21st century, the trend of aging population has laid a hidden danger of the lack of labor force, and energy conservation has become an increasingly urgent demand. This is not only an empty slogan but also requires the manufacturing industry to further accelerate the automation process and control the details of production and management more accurately and carefully, so as to achieve the purpose of improving energy efficiency. Against this background, it is clearly not a good idea to continue to dump long and rigid production lines into long and complex processes, with people constantly adjusting through the trial-and-error method. Whether in efficiency or in effect, this kind of people-centered adjustment management mechanism will find it difficult to keep pace with the ever-changing demand pace.

Intelligent manufacturing systems have the support of advanced information technology, which gives the manufacturing industry a level of flexibility and sophistication that it hasn't had in the past. One important reason for that is it has won the 6M outside the five core elements for manufacturing, namely Modeling (data and knowledge modeling, including monitoring, prediction, optimization and protection, etc.), as shown in Fig. 2.3.

Through the 6M, the original five elements can be effectively driven to solve and avoid problems and hazards in the manufacturing process. Compared with the idea of solving problems in the traditional manufacturing industry, the basic logic of operation in the era of intelligent

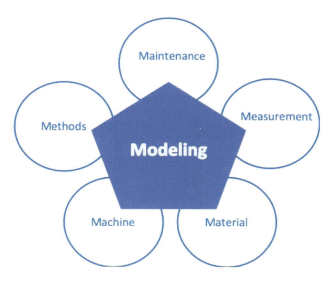

Figure 2.3 6M elements of intelligent manufacturing.

manufacturing should be: Finding problems → Analyzing problems through models → Adjusting five elements in the models → Problem solving → Accumulating model experience and analyzing the root cause of problems → Adjusting five elements in the models → Avoiding problems.

As you can see, the new problem to be solved by intelligent manufacturing is to optimize the process of knowledge generation and transmission. This is precisely the current forefront of an important direction of the development of computer science. The advent of 5G maximizes all speed requirements of intelligent manufacturing, while bringing a whole new look to the relationship between factories, equipment, consumers, and managers. The problems of development will be solved by development, and the demands of the new era will be met by the technology of the new era. If the increasingly tricky market demands confuse the manufacturing industry practitioners, then it may be a good way for the factory and equipment to start "high-speed thinking and join communication" together.

Of course, it's always easy to come up with ideas. So in the following section, we look at the specific features and implications of intelligent manufacturing.

2.2 How Intelligent Is Intelligent Manufacturing?

2.2.1 *The characteristics of intelligent manufacturing*

Before delving further into intelligent manufacturing, let's set up a simple scenario:

Sara wants to buy an office equipment A for her office. As an artistic youth, Sara's requirements for office equipment are also very interesting. The appearance should meet her own aesthetic taste, and the functions she doesn't want should not exist. With these needs in mind, she decides on a strange color and excitedly went to the web page to start picking out products, only to be greeted with disappointing results. First of all, in the range of products in her budget, there are almost two choices in terms of color, but there is nothing she wants. Second, when she managed to find a simple and elegant product that is exactly what she wanted, she found that it is out of stock. With Sara's persistent questioning, the customer service staff gives an explanation: originally the plant's main product is of another kind, office equipment B, so the factory production lines are mostly for the production of equipment B, but this month, the sales volume of equipment A is unexpectedly much higher than that of equipment B. The manufacturer doesn't have so many production lines to produce equipment A in a short time, which led to the shortage of the equipment.

Although this is a fictional example, the feeling of facing a situation in which the things you can get are out of stock or not being able to fully satisfy your purchase needs must be familiar to all of us. From this example, we can raise the following questions about the improvement of the manufacturing process:

(1) Can we achieve more segmented customized manufacturing for more products and provide customers with personalized customized products?
(2) Can different production lines of the factory be adjusted quickly and integrated flexibly to keep up with the changing demand and keep the cost low enough?
(3) Can we use flexible production methods such as robots, intelligent machine tools, and 3D printing to make the production line of mass rigid production "flexible"?
(4) Once a large number of intelligent devices are used, massive data will inevitably be generated, and it is necessary to monitor, analyze, and make decisions. Can the equipment and technology of the factory provide high-performance communication and computing support?

20 *The World of 5G: Intelligent Manufacturing*

Figure 2.4 Effect diagram of intelligent manufacturing.

These simple questions are far from enough to clearly express the tasks to be realized by intelligent manufacturing. We can only use them to plan the outline of intelligent manufacturing, so as to lead to the picture of an intelligent factory and several characteristics that make intelligent manufacturing "intelligent", as shown in Fig. 2.4.

It can be seen that compared with factories in the Industry 3.0 era, intelligent factories will absorb more achievements of information development. They will start from the foundation of digital factories, integrate communication technology and artificial intelligence technology, and use the IoT and device perception monitoring system to build a powerful intelligent service function and information management network, which can greatly improve the flexibility, controllability, and automation of the production and production management process. Meanwhile, they'll effectively design and manage manufacturing processes using the ability to quickly and accurately access production line data together to integrate a green factory which can "think" for future needs through more environmentally friendly and energy-efficient equipment and manufacturing methods.

To be precise, a smart factory is not exactly equivalent to an intelligent manufacturing system, but it is one of the most intuitive examples of how intelligent manufacturing can be projected into real-world operations. When the hierarchical operation picture of an intelligent factory is outlined, we can summarize some characteristics of intelligent manufacturing that are different from traditional manufacturing to see what kind of "character" and "skill" a manufacturing system like a human can have. The ideal intelligent manufacturing system has the characteristics of self-discipline, learning and self-maintenance, man–machine integration, virtual reality (VR) technology, self-organizing, and super-flexibility.

1. Self-discipline: Self-discipline can be understood as the ability to take the initiative to observe and analyze specific situations and make active plans according to one's own state. Machines in intelligent manufacturing systems can actively collect and understand information — including information related to the environment and themselves in the process — and analyze, judge, and plan their own behavior. This ability is based on the massive knowledge base and the establishment of the learning model for the knowledge base. With the ability of self-discipline, the equipment can operate autonomously, coordinate, and even compete with each other, showing a high degree of independence. This kind of highly independent device is called an "intelligent machine".

2. Learning and self-maintenance ability: This kind of ability is also related to the knowledge base and learning model, but it differs from the self-discipline ability in that the learning and self-maintenance ability of the intelligent manufacturing system not only applies to the knowledge base now but also reflects the continuous expansion of the knowledge base in practice according to the actual situation and needs and has the self-learning function. This ability is especially important when manufacturing operations encounter unexpected failures, and intelligent machines can use this ability to self-diagnose, troubleshoot, and maintain their own. Like human beings, machines in intelligent manufacturing systems are often faced with complex, diverse, and dynamic environments. Therefore, it is very important for both humans and intelligent machines to have the ability to optimize and adjust themselves at any time.

3. Man–machine integration: An intelligent manufacturing system that can "think" will not be "arrogant", and it and the intelligent devices within it will certainly have a need to collaborate with people. This "cooperation" is known as human–machine integration, which represents the combination of artificial intelligence and human intelligence. One of the foundations of smart devices is artificial intelligence, so they can be trained to "think logically" and make judgments based on experience. However, due to the limited development of artificial intelligence, the scope and freedom of thinking have not been fully opened. For example, it is still unable to achieve "insight" like a human, so it cannot completely replace a human to make analysis, thinking, and judgment independently in all circumstances in manufacturing activities. Therefore, the cooperation between intelligent devices and human experts is essential in intelligent manufacturing systems. On the one hand, of course, this man–machine integration has a face-saving feature that preserves the central role of human thinking in manufacturing decisions. On the other hand, with the cooperation of intelligent devices, people can also reach their full potential. It can be said that this kind of man–machine integration enables both of them to have the relationship of "equal cooperation", and both of them have rooms to play in the aspects they are good at.

4. Virtual reality technology: The concept of simulation is often used in the process of product design. The common purpose is to verify the actual effect or function of product design in a virtual way. Virtual reality technology is a powerful technology based on computer, integrating signal processing, animation technology, intelligent reasoning, prediction, simulation, and multimedia technology. It takes the range and depth of simulation to another level. Using an intelligent machine with virtual reality technology, we can achieve virtual manufacturing, which is one of the key scenarios representing the highest level of man–machine integration. In this kind of scene, we can use various audio-visual and sensing devices to virtual display the realization situation of the manufacturing plan on the actual production line, experience the products produced by virtual production, and get a similar real feeling from the senses. It can also be used to meet the needs of remote debugging and operation by human intervention, simulating real operation scenarios for operators, and applying the simulated scenarios to real scenes after verification. This new generation of intelligent interface, which combines man and machine, is a remarkable feature of intelligent manufacturing system.

5. Self-organizing hyperflexibility: The equipment in intelligent manufacturing system has not only individual operation intelligence but also the characteristics of intelligent group. This is reflected in that all components in the system can analyze the needs of the specific tasks independently and construct the optimal way of coordination, and its flexibility is manifested in both operation mode and combination mode, so it is called super-flexibility, just like a force that is well trained and flexible enough to assemble and accomplish specific tasks as needed. As you can imagine, when the intelligent manufacturing system is confronted with a problem like the production line configuration not keeping up with the shipment demand as discussed at the beginning of this section, it can quickly and autonomously carry out efficient restructuring of the component production line to flexibly respond to the changes in the shipment demand for a variety of products. This is the charm of the self-organized super-flexibility.

2.2.2 *The performance of intelligent manufacturing*

In general, the connotations and requirements of intelligent manufacturing include five aspects: intellectualization of product, intellectualization of equipment, intellectualization of production mode, intellectualization of management, and intellectualization of service.

1. Intellectualization of a product: Intellectualization of a product requires the integration of sensors, processors, memory, communication modules, and transmission systems with various products to enable the products to have dynamic storage, perception and communication capabilities, and to realize traceability, identification, and positioning of products, as shown in Fig. 2.5. According to the concept of the Internet of

Figure 2.5   Smart home products.

Things, computers, smartphones, smart TVs, smart robots, and smart wearables are all the most basic connected entities. It can be said that they are "born" as a network terminal that can be easily connected. The smart manufacturing plan also targets the production of more traditional products that can be upgraded to smart connectivity, including air conditioners, refrigerators, cars, machine tools, etc., all of which need to be connected to the IoT in the smart manufacturing production line.

2. Intellectualization of equipment: Intellectualization of equipment does not denote a simple individual intelligent machine, but generally refers to the intelligent manufacturing systems with self-organizing and adaptive functions (perception, analysis, reasoning, decision-making, execution, independent learning, and maintenance) and networked and collaborative production facilities through the integration and fusion of advanced manufacturing, information processing, artificial intelligence, and other technologies. Therefore, in the era of intelligent manufacturing, the process of intelligent equipment can be carried out in two dimensions: first, the intelligent single machine; second, intelligent production line, intelligent workshop, and intelligent factory formed through the interconnection of standalone equipment. It is necessary to point out that the intellectualization process of equipment is not only the transformation of research and development and production end but also the transformation and integration of the channel and consumer insight management system. The combination of the two can be regarded as an intelligent transformation of the whole chain of equipment.

3. Intellectualization of production mode: The intellectualization of production mode refers to the creation of new business forms and models, such as personalized customization, minimal production, service-oriented manufacturing, and cloud manufacturing in the intelligent manufacturing system. The essence of promoting the formation of these new modes is to reorganize the relationships among customers, suppliers, distributors, and internal organizations of enterprises, reconstruct the operation modes of information flow, product flow and capital flow in the production system, and rebuild the new industrial value chain, ecosystem and competition pattern. In the traditional industrial era, enterprises define product value, decide what products customers can find in the market, and have completely independent pricing power, which means that the initiative is completely in the hands of enterprises. While intelligent manufacturing can achieve personalized customization, remove the intermediate link, and enrich the form of commercial flow. Product value is no longer defined by the enterprises alone, but defined by the customers comprehensively involved in the conception, design, production, after-sales, and other aspects of the products.

4. Intellectualization of management: Intellectualization of management can be well represented in the optimization of all operational levels by the intelligent factory introduced in the first half of this section. The management system of intelligent manufacturing will continue to deepen in vertical integration, horizontal integration, and end-to-end integration, pursuing the continuous improvement of timeliness, integrity, and accuracy of enterprise data, and establishing a more accurate, more efficient, and more scientific intelligent management system, as shown in Fig. 2.6.

5. Intellectualization of service: Intelligent service is the core content of intelligent manufacturing. More and more manufacturing enterprises have realized the importance of transforming from production-oriented manufacturing to production service manufacturing. In the future, O2O (Online-to-Offline) services will be implemented in parallel with online and offline services. Two forces are moving in the same direction in terms of service intelligence: one is expanding services in traditional manufacturing, and the other is the turning of the consumer Internet into an industrial Internet. For example, WeChat will connect not just people and people, but devices and devices, services and services, and people and services. Personalized R&D and design and the whole life cycle management of new service products, such as general integration and general contracting, will continue to appear along with the reform of production mode.

From the above introduction of characteristics, connotations, and requirements of intelligent manufacturing, we can see that intelligent manufacturing is indeed a significant upgrade of the existing manufacturing industry. First of all, it pursues the use of virtual manufacturing technology to simulate the whole life cycle of the product in the product design stage, so as to reduce the product cost and improve the product quality while pursuing the shortest product development cycle. Secondly, it promotes the manufacturing industry to develop a new manufacturing mode, including flexible manufacturing, biological manufacturing, green manufacturing, etc. Flexible manufacturing is one of its iconic features, which pursues

26 *The World of 5G: Intelligent Manufacturing*

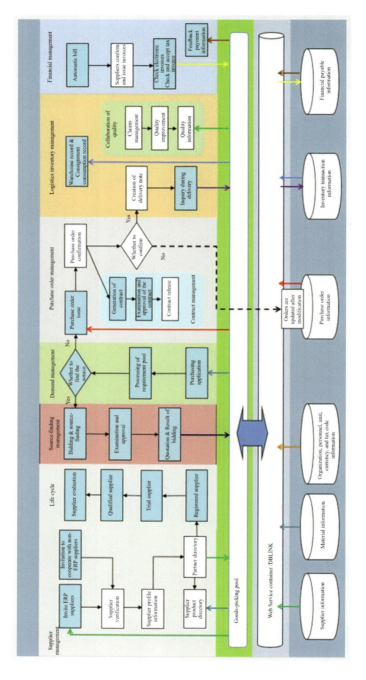

Figure 2.6 Intelligent management platform.

customization. This consumer-oriented quantitative and flexible production mode can well distinguish intelligent manufacturing from the traditional manufacturing system represented by mass production mode. Finally, intelligent manufacturing will promote the formation of a large number of intelligent manufacturing equipment industries. The scope of the application industry includes all kinds of light industry, heavy industry, and logistics industry, which is of great significance for intelligent manufacturing in promoting economic development.

2.3 How to Achieve Intelligent Manufacturing

The functional design of an intelligent manufacturing system aims to use some core technologies to automatically identify and deal with various situations, to conduct information fusion analysis through wireless sensor networks, to solve problems flexibly, and to achieve the purpose of eliminating hidden dangers of network security scientifically and reasonably. Therefore, to comprehensively understand intelligent manufacturing, in addition to its characteristics and connotations, we also need to understand the key technologies supporting the whole huge system, as they are all important links in the production process of intelligent manufacturing. In recent years, the research and development and gradual application of 5G communication technology have provided strong data and network support for the technical system of intelligent manufacturing.

Let's take a look at the key technologies involved in intelligent manufacturing systems.

1. Recognition technology: An intelligent function is a key link in the process of intelligent manufacturing, so the identification technology required mainly includes radio frequency identification technology, 3D image recognition technology, etc.

Radio Frequency Identification (RFID) is a kind of wireless communication technology. The non-contact two-way data communication is carried out by means of radio frequency, and the recording media (electronic tag or radio frequency card) is read and written, so as to achieve the purpose of target identification and data exchange. Radio frequency can be divided into three types, namely, low frequency, high frequency and ultra-high frequency, and RFID readers can be divided into two types (mobile and fixed). RFID reader can be attached to the object surface, can

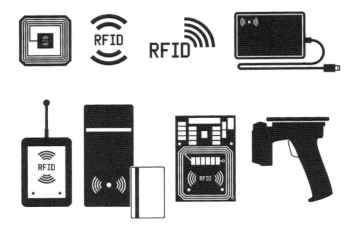

Figure 2.7 Application of RFID technology.

automatically read and recognize radio signals from a long distance, and can be used as a fast, accurate record and collection device. RFID has the characteristics of non-contact, high efficiency (the transfer time is usually less than 100 ms), uniqueness (every RFID tag is unique and corresponds to only one product), and simplicity. Its application greatly simplifies the process of object recording, identification, monitoring, and tracking involved in intelligent manufacturing and forms the basis of the tracking management system, as shown in Fig. 2.7.

The task of 3D image object recognition is to identify the number and type of the object in the image and accurately describe the position of the object in the actual environment. The essence of this technology is the perception and understanding of the 3D environment. On this basis, it can further evaluate the detailed state of the object according to the image to judge whether there are defects. This is an application combining artificial intelligence science, computer science, and information science.

2. Real-time positioning and wireless sensing systems: In the process of production, it is necessary to accurately and clearly grasp the location of products in production as well as the storage location of materials, parts, and tools. Real-Time Location System (RTLS) can track and manage all raw materials, parts, tools, equipment, and other production materials in real time during the whole process of product manufacturing.

In the actual manufacturing site, the usual practice is to attach active RFID tags to the tracking target and then place more than three reader antennas in the room, so that the tracking target can be conveniently located and queried. The broadcast signal system sends the signal to all the antennas of the reader. After the signal is sent out, the measurement and calculation can be conducted through the target location. Both inside and outside the building, RTLS can be used for identification and real-time tracking to determine the target location of the object. The physical layer technology of RTLS is a concrete application example of using Radio Frequency (RF) to communicate.

3. Cyber-physical system: Relative to the RF and real-time positioning system, the cyber-physical system is a large multidimensional complex system which can fully represent intelligent manufacturing. It can combine computing, networking, and physical environment and realize real-time perception, dynamic control, and information service of a large engineering system through the organic integration and deep collaboration of 3C (Computation, Communication, and Control) technologies. This is the technical core of the intelligent manufacturing system, as shown in Fig. 2.8.

A cyber-physical system can be summarized as a distributed heterogeneous system integrating physical process and computing process,

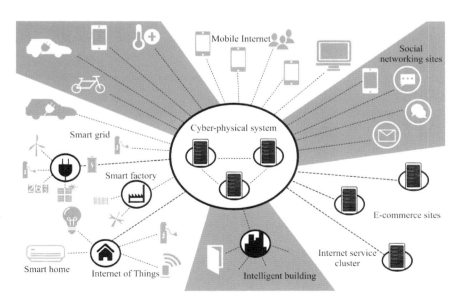

Figure 2.8   Cyber-physical system.

which can make full use of the sensor network and data science to achieve a more intelligent distributed real-time control and has the characteristics of adaptability, autonomy, high efficiency, functionality, reliability, security, and so on. Physical and software builds must be able to dynamically join the system without shutting down or stopping, ensuring that both system requirements and quality of service are met. For example, a security system for supermarkets can be dynamically upgraded without shutting down the whole system during the process of adding physical nodes such as sensors, cameras, and monitors or conducting software upgrades. In addition, CPS should be an intelligent system with autonomous behaviors. CPS can not only obtain data from the environment, do data fusion and extract effective information but also exert effects on the environment through actuators according to system rules.

After the cyber-physical system is applied to intelligent manufacturing, a processing device can count the types, quantity, and processing methods of the currently processed parts, and a part can calculate which processing procedures and which processing equipment are required by itself. In addition, through the automatic upgrading of production facilities, the system architecture of the production system can be easily changed. This means that existing factories can be upgraded from rigid central industrial control systems to intelligent distributed control systems, with sensors that accurately record the environment of everything and a separate embedded processor system in the production control center to make decisions.

This process involves the application of a number of more advanced wireless sensor systems. There are many detection points distributed in large manufacturing enterprises, and they will automatically collect a large number of production-related data, while the wireless sensor network in intelligent manufacturing is distributed in multiple spaces, which will form a wireless communication computer network system to process the massive data generated. The functional layer of the wireless sensor system mainly includes three aspects: physical induction, information transmission, and calculation and positioning. It can make physical responses to different objects and environments, such as temperature, pressure, sound, vibration, and pollutants. Wireless database technology is the key technology of a wireless sensor system, including technologies like query wireless sensor network, information transfer network, and multiple hop routing protocol.

Under the condition of real-time sensing of the production process by a wireless sensor system, CPS can realize dynamic management and information service and can be applied in the integrated design of computing, communication, and physical system. The process of embedding computation and communication in the physical object enriches the interaction in intelligent manufacturing and the usage of the physical system.

4. Network security technology: There are a lot of applications of computer network technology and Big Data technology in intelligent manufacturing, which makes network security technology an essential link. In an intelligent manufacturing factory, automatic machines and sensors can be seen everywhere, and a large amount of information will be processed every moment. The whole process of product design, manufacturing, and service can be presented with digital technical data, and the information generated by the whole supply chain can be shared through the computer network. In order to protect the network system and the information involved in these processes, IT-guaranteed technology and relevant security measures can be adopted, such as firewall, prevention of intrusion, scanning virus instrument, control access, the establishment of black and white list, and encryption information.

5. System collaboration technology: Large-scale intelligent manufacturing engineering projects often need a variety of technologies to work together to complete them, such as overall scheme design technology of complex automation system, installation and debugging technology, design technology of unified operation interface and engineering tools, unified event sequence and alarm processing technology, and integrated asset management technology. System collaboration technology can standardize and define important details such as time sequence, event, conflict, request, and man–machine interface scheduling, involved in the common application of multiple technologies and further enhance the standardization, security, and convenience of operation management of the intelligent manufacturing process.

From these key technologies of intelligent manufacturing, it is not difficult for us to realize the significance of 5G to the upgrade of intelligent manufacturing, because the efficient communication between massive sensors, production equipment, cloud computing platform, products, and production materials is the basis for the realization of these key technologies. Intelligent manufacturing has extremely demanding and diversified functional requirements for a communication network. On the one hand, the intelligent manufacturing system needs to support high-precision production with massive data, and the information transmission delay involved in the process must be controlled in a very low range to ensure the accuracy of perception, decision, and control. Therefore, the whole process requires a highly reliable network to ensure the safety and efficiency of the manufacturing process. On the other hand, the span of work scenes of factory automation control system and sensing system is very big and may involve distributed deployment; there may be tens of thousands of sensors and actuators in the factory production area. This put forward high requirements for the connection capacity of the communication network and the consistency of the performance in a large range of coverage.

2.4 The Demand of Intelligent Manufacturing for New Networks

The integration of the new generation of information and communication technology with the manufacturing industry has gradually shifted from concept popularization to application promotion. The transformation and development trend of the manufacturing industry is becoming more and more obvious, and the demand for the wireless network with high performance and flexible networking ability is becoming increasingly urgent. The traditional industrial network has some problems, such as unstable time delay, data isolation, and security risk. Due to different industrial Fieldbus protocol standards, different manufacturers cannot communicate with each other, so the equipment status cannot be effectively monitored. Thus, enterprises need to invest a lot of manpower and material resources in production planning, material distribution, production collaboration, quality control, equipment testing, and other links. The traditional IP (Internet Protocol) network uses the best-effort transmission mechanism, so the time delay is unstable and has packet loss, which cannot be used in some time-sensitive scenarios. At the same time, network security problems emerge endlessly, and industrial control equipment is generally not patched. Once the equipment is connected to the outside of the network, it is easy to be invaded and attacked, which then brings great losses for enterprises.

What the new network needs to solve is not only the connection problem between people but also the connection problem between people and things, and between things. The network communication of intelligent manufacturing application has two kinds of transmission modes: the wired communication methods are industrial PON (passive optical network) and Ethernet network communication technology; wireless communication means are 4G, 5G, Wi-Fi, NB-IoT, LoRa, ZigBee, and other network technologies. The future development of the integrated industrial Internet puts forward the following technical requirements for the new network:

1. Transmission rate requirement: The transmission rate is required to be increased by 10–100 times, while the user experience rate and user peak rate should be 0. 1–1 Gb/s and 10 Gb/s, respectively.

2. Time delay requirement: It requires the delay to be reduced to 10–20%, up to the millisecond level. It can meet the application network transmission capacity of industrial real-time control, cloud robot, etc., to ensure that the control instructions and data of the system can be sent to the equipment in time, thus achieving reliable and safe production and operation process.

3. Requirements for connection density of devices: The connection density of equipment is required to be increased by 10–100 times to 6 million units per square kilometer. It can satisfy the cooperation of human, machine, and object as well as the network connection ability of multi-machine cooperation of automated-guided vehicle (AGV), which can satisfy the flexible production of equipment and improve the production efficiency.

4. Flow density requirement: The flow density is required to be increased by 100–1,000 times to 20 TB/(s · km^2). It can achieve the purposes of industrial cooperative operation guidance, expert system development, Big Data analysis, and calculation by combining AI and remote communication technology, such as intelligent monitoring and digital twinning.

5. Security requirement: In the face of various application scenarios and business requirements, it is necessary to establish a new network security architecture to meet the security requirements of different security levels in different applications.

Thus, the new network plays a crucial role in the development of intelligent manufacturing, and the 5G network with high speed, low delay, and extensive connection can well meet this demand.

Intelligent manufacturing is the core business of the Fourth Industrial Revolution. The application of Internet, cloud computing, artificial intelligence, Big Data, and other technologies has brought revolutionary upgrades to intelligent manufacturing.

Chapter 3

5G Upgrade of Intelligent Manufacturing: A Major Opportunity for Industrial Upgrading

The rapid development of today's 5G technology simply meets the application requirements of intelligent manufacturing for a wireless network. The three application scenarios defined by 5C technology (eMBB, mMTC, and uRLLC) not only cover traditional application scenarios with the requirements of high rate and low delay but also meet the application requirements of equipment interconnection and remote interaction in an industrial environment. This feature of full coverage of a wide "domain network" provides the possibility for enterprises to build a unified wireless network, so that a variety of intelligent manufacturing scenarios can be realized, such as logistics tracking, IoT, industrial augmented reality (AR)/ virtual reality (VR), automation control, and cloud robot. This has a positive significance for promoting the implementation of industrial Internet and deepening the transformation of intelligent manufacturing. It can be said that 5G technology has become the key technology to support the transformation of intelligent manufacturing.

The international standardization organization 3GPP defines the following three application scenarios for 5G: eMBB (Enhanced Mobile Broadband) — 3D/UHD video and other high-throughput enhanced mobile broadband services; uRLLC (Ultra-Reliable Low-latency Communications) — unmanned driving, industrial automation, and other services that require high reliability and low-latency

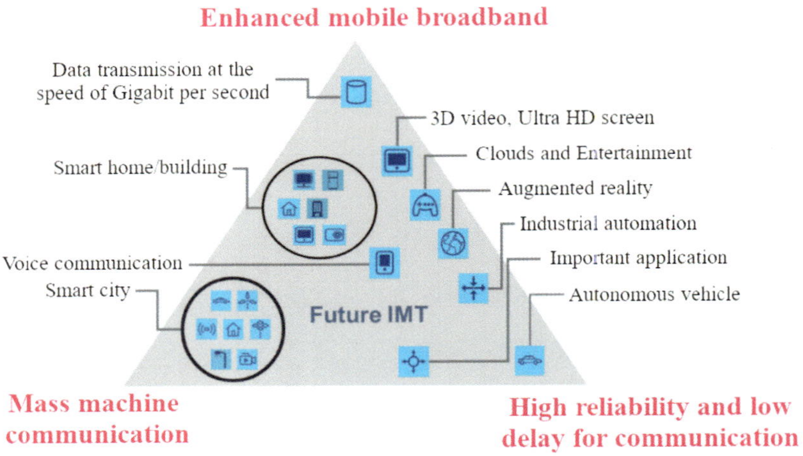

36　*The World of 5G: Intelligent Manufacturing*

Figure 3.1　Three application scenarios of 5G.

connections; mMTC (Massive Machine Type Communication) — the large-scale IoT business, as shown in Fig. 3.1.

3.1　5G+ The Overall Architecture of Intelligent Manufacturing

The 5G network has seen an expansion from traditional people-centered services to material-centered services. High speed, low latency, and high reliability unique to the industrial sector enabled wireless technology to be applied in real-time control, remote maintenance and control of field devices, industrial high-definition image processing, and other new industrial areas. Meanwhile, it also laid the foundation for the establishment of flexible production lines and flexible workshops in the future. 5G is more widely applied in intelligent manufacturing, opening up prospects for wireless development in the industrial sector. China is quickly becoming a manufacturing power while advancing intelligent manufacturing, which will see a wider and more in-depth application of 5G. 5G+ the overall architecture of intelligent manufacturing mainly includes the following four layers: data layer, network layer, platform layer, and application layer, as shown in Fig. 3.2.

5G Upgrade of Intelligent Manufacturing 37

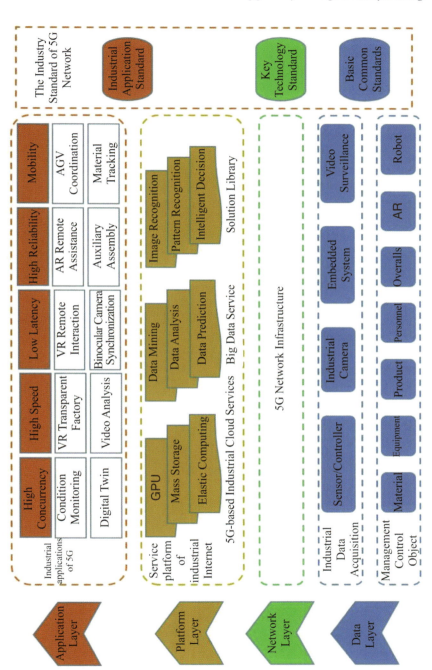

Figure 3.2 5G+ the overall architecture of intelligent manufacturing.

3.1.1 *Data layer*

The data layer collects real-time data, including equipment status, the workshop's working conditions, operating environment, production data, as well as operation and maintenance services and management information generated by managerial and maintenance personnel. Basically, this layer uses sensor technology to collect real-time data and gather on the cloud the information elements, including multi-source equipment, heterogeneous systems, operating environment, and personnel, within the factory to build a real-time, efficient, and accurate data collection system. At the same time, with protocol conversion and edge computing technologies, some of the collected data are analyzed and processed on the edge, and the results are directly returned to the device to guide device operation; the remaining data will be transmitted to the cloud for comprehensive analysis and processing and better decision-making. The data layer makes the implicit data of the whole manufacturing process explicit and provides a massive amount of data sources for the optimization of manufacturing resources. It is the starting point for real-time analysis and sound decision-making and the foundation for building an Internet service platform for the intelligent manufacturing industry.

3.1.2 *Network layer*

The network layer guarantees better services for the platform layer and application layer. As the enterprises' network resource, the construction of 5G network infrastructure serves as the core and link of intelligent manufacturing and a strong support for realizing world-class intelligent manufacturing. The 5G network with wide-range connection and low latency connects a large number of production devices and key components in the factory, promptly collects the production data, and offers network support for production process optimization and energy consumption management. In addition, a great number of sensors in the factory can report the information status in a very short time through the 5G network, allowing the managerial staff to accurately control the environment in the factory. At the same time, the 5G network can synchronously transmit the high-resolution surveillance video in the factory back to the control center and reveal the production details of all areas through the ultra-high-definition video to support the factory's delicacy monitoring and management.

Moreover, in the factory, product defect detection, fine raw material identification, and precision measurement require three-dimensional image recognition technologies. The 5G network ensures the real-time transmission of tons of high-resolution video images and improves the recognition speed and accuracy of the machine's vision system. In the meantime, the 5G network is helpful for real-time, full life-cycle monitoring of the working status of remote production equipment, enabling remote fault diagnosis and maintenance across factories and regions.

3.1.3 *Platform layer*

The 5G technology-based construction of the platform layer is essential for further upgrading intelligent manufacturing, which mainly includes industrial cloud services featuring graphics processing unit (GPU), mass storage, and elastic computing, Big Data services featuring data mining, data analysis, and data prediction, and solution library featuring image recognition, pattern recognition, and intelligent decision-making. 5G-based cloud services, among others, can provide convenient interfaces for the development, testing, and deployment of industrial apps and realize further upgrading of research and applications. Meanwhile, Big Data services based on 5G and industrial Internet platforms are able to build real-time Most Significant Bit (MSB) so as to realize superfast transmission of key technologies. Furthermore, image recognition, pattern recognition, and intelligent decision-making can be easily integrated into the factory's solution library with a combination of advanced 5G and artificial intelligence technologies at home and abroad.

3.1.4 *Application layer*

The application layer realizes technology transfer of intelligent manufacturing technology based on 5G, including typical products and industry solutions. High speed, low latency, and wide-range connection enable the 5G network to develop a series of industry applications to help enterprises become more digitalized and intelligent. Status monitoring, digital twins, VR transparent factories, video analysis, VR remote interaction, binocular camera synchronization, AR remote assistance, auxiliary assembly, automated guided vehicle (AGV) coordination, material tracking, etc., are relatively common application scenarios. At the same time, 5G will be

40 *The World of 5G: Intelligent Manufacturing*

applied in more industrial sectors to make 5G+ industry application terminals, systems, and supporting software. After that, various scenarios will be added to provide users with personalized, precise, and intelligent services for the in-depth empowerment of intelligent manufacturing.

3.2 5G+ Key Technologies of Intelligent Manufacturing

5G boasts of high speed, low latency, and wide-range connection that meet industrial Internet's network demands of diverse connection, differentiated performance, and diversified communication, boosting the supply capacity of the Industrial Internet, providing solid technology support for the leapfrog development of the industrial Internet and fully supporting the innovative development of the industrial Internet's new businesses and models. 5G+ intelligent manufacturing has the following key technologies.

3.2.1 *5G TSN (time-sensitive networking) technology*

High-precision time synchronization enables wireless TSN in the factory that ensures end-to-end low-latency of industrial Internet businesses.

3.2.2 *Network slicing technology*

5G network slicing technology supports the isolation and protection of various business scenarios, services and quality, and multiple users and industries. 5G's high-frequency and multi-antenna technology support precise positioning and high-bandwidth communications in the factory, significantly improving operation accuracy in remote control.

To provide broad access to and extensive coverage of the industrial Internet, the communication technology involved must target different user terminals, deliver differentiated services, and optimize resource allocation based on user needs in different scenarios. Network slicing is a key technology for 5G networks on demand allocation. 5G has to adapt to three different application scenarios eMBB, uRLLC, and mMTC at the same time. eMBB requires fast network signal transmission, uRLLC requires highly reliable network transmission with low latency, and under the mMTC scenario, the network has to be able to support dense and

5G Upgrade of Intelligent Manufacturing 41

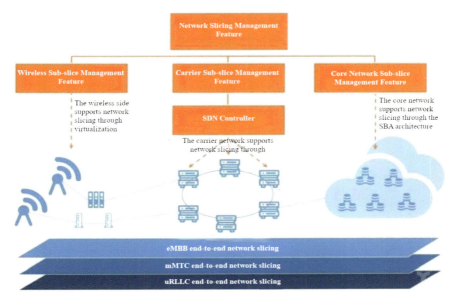

Figure 3.3 Network slicing management architecture.

various kinds of access terminals. It is difficult for today's technology to meet all the business requirements by using the same network and the same signal with exactly the same characteristics. Network slicing technology was born right at this moment. The technology supports eMBB, uRLLC, and mMTC, respectively, to realize the on-demand allocation of 5G network slices where the end-to-end system operates, as shown in Fig. 3.3. Based on different scenarios and businesses, network slicing can apply and deploy different network logical functions and flexibly arrange network architecture and functions on a common network platform, so as to arrange scenarios tailored to specific businesses, offer information network with distinctive characteristics to different users, and provide network services that meet the needs of specific user terminals.

3.2.3 *Mobile edge computing (MEC) technology*

5G edge computing accelerates the integration of industrial IT and OT (Operational Technology) networks, enhances edge data processing, tracking and aggregation capabilities, contributes to higher reliability and

42 *The World of 5G: Intelligent Manufacturing*

lower latency of industrial Internet services, and optimizes resource sharing and user experience.

MEC is short for multi-access edge computing. The technology supports multiple accesses, such as 5G, Wi-Fi, and fixed networks, while reducing transmission delay and easing network congestion to deploy services under distributed conditions and offers edge intelligent services nearby. MEC provides user-friendly cloud computing capabilities and manages third-party application resources based on the virtualized software environment provided by network function virtualization (NFV). The third-party application is deployed on the edge cloud in the form of a virtual machine and obtains wireless network capabilities through a unified service open framework.

MEC enables operators and third-party businesses to be deployed close to the user's attached access point to achieve efficient business distribution by reducing latency and load. MEC is able to cover the three major 5G application scenarios for the industrial Internet. Traffic distribution and traffic offload on eMBB reduce network bandwidth pressure; moving down 5G user plane and building edge DC on uRLLC offer an improved network performance; local analysis, mobility, and auxiliary information for session management on mMTC reduce the pressure on the central unit.

3.2.4 *Industrial cloud platform technology*

To build a digital, networked, and intelligent manufacturing industry, the industrial cloud platform technology establishes a service system based on massive data collection, aggregation, and analysis and an industrial cloud platform to support the ubiquitous connection, flexible supply, and efficient allocation of manufacturing resources, including three core levels edge, platform as a service (PaaS), and application. Basically, the industrial cloud platform technology adds emerging technologies such as the IoT, Big Data, and artificial intelligence to traditional cloud platforms to build a more accurate, real-time, and efficient data collection system and an enabling platform that integrates storage, integration, access, analysis, and management features to realize the modeling, software-oriented application, and reuse of industrial technologies, experience and knowledge and provides various kinds of innovative applications in the form of industrial apps for manufacturers. Ultimately, intelligent manufacturing featuring rich resources, multi-party participation, win–win cooperation, and collaborative evolution will become a reality.

3.2.5 *5G network security technology*

3.2.5.1 *Intelligent terminal security*

The 5G network has to support the access of different types of terminals with different access types and technologies, as they have varied security requirements. The general requirements of 5G terminal security include confidentiality protection of user signaling data, safe storage and processing of signing vouchers, and user privacy protection. The special requirements of 5G terminal security include the following: (1) uRLLC terminal needs to support a highly secure and reliable security mechanism; (2) mMTC terminal needs to support lightweight security algorithms and protocols; (3) the manufacturing industry requires customized security chips, operating systems, and application stores.

The security architecture introduces the security side in the terminal. On the terminal security side, the information storage, computing environment, and standardized security interface are built to ensure terminal security from both the terminal itself and the external environment. The terminal can enhance its own security protection capabilities by building a trusted storage and computing environment; as for the external environment, standardized security interfaces are introduced to support the introduction of third-party security services and security modules as well as cloud-based security enhancement mechanisms to provide auxiliary features such as security monitoring, security analysis, and security management, thereby ensuring terminal security.

3.2.5.2 *Network information security*

(1) *Data access security*: Industrial firewall technology, industrial GAP technology, and encrypted tunnel transmission technology prevent data leaks, interception or tampering, and ensure data safety at the source and during transmission.
(2) *Platform security*: Real-time platform intrusion detection, network security defensive system, malicious code protection, website threat protection, webpage anti-tampering, and other technologies realize

code security, application security, data security, and website security of the industrial Internet platform.

(3) *Access security*: Access control and management of important resources on the cloud platform can be realized and illegal access can be prevented by establishing a unified access mechanism and limiting users' access rights and available computing and network resources.

3.3 5G+ Examples of Intelligent Manufacturing Exploration

5G+ intelligent manufacturing is well received worldwide. For example, Worcester Bosch launched the UK's first 5G factory at Worcester Polytechnic Institute. South Korean operators have introduced 5G services in some parts of the country, and the South Korean industrial sector collaborated with 19 companies and organizations including SK Telecom, Samsung Electronics, Microsoft Korea, LG, and Siemens Korea to set up a 5G intelligent factory alliance. Chinese operators have also provided 5G services to factories such as China Mobile and Ericsson who jointly launched pilot projects for 5G intelligent factory renovation and application. China Unicom set up the China Unicom 5G Industrial Internet Industry Alliance by collaborating with 46 academies and companies, including the Chinese Academy of Sciences, Haier Digital, Gree, FOTON, Foxconn, and XCMG Information.

3.3.1 *Examples of South Korea's exploration*

South Korea's manufacturing industry has made remarkable strides in 5G+ intelligent manufacturing. In December 2018, three major Korean operators SK Telecom, KT, and LG announced the launch of 5G services in part of the country. Since 5G commercial intelligent terminals are not available, most 5G users in South Korea are enterprises. 5G Intelligent Factory Alliance plans to build 30,000 intelligent factories and 10 intelligent industrial zones by 2022.

SK Telecom's 5G factory solutions include multifunctional robots, intelligent production equipment, small-sized self-driving robots, augmented reality glasses, and 5G+ AI machine vision. SK Telecom's first 5G user is Myunghwa Industry, an auto parts company. The 5G factory uses the 5G network to transmit high-definition pictures and videos on the production line to the cloud server, AI will then analyze the images, and "5G+ AI machine vision" will check if the product is defective to improve the production quality of the production line. As the auto parts pass through the conveyor belt, a 12-megapixel camera will take 24 photos from all directions. When the pictures are sent to the cloud server through the 5G network, AI will read the pictures while checking for defects before informing the result, and the robotic arm will automatically filter out defective products. The process only takes less than 8s. SK Telecom's "5G+ AI machine vision" technology takes advantage of 5G's high reliability and low latency, along with AI and MEC to realize the high speed operation of the production process. Using "5G+ AI machine vision" technology instead of workers to check for defects could double the per capita production capacity.

KT's 5G technology was first applied to the 5G shipyard of Hyundai Heavy Industries (HHI). Through networked monitors and AR glasses, various problems in HHI's production sites and factory operations can be solved. For example, using AR glasses for error checking and real-time monitoring of the production site, the shipowner can confirm in real time the actual condition of the ship ordered.

3.3.2 *Examples of China's exploration*

Operators in China are also putting forward 5G+ intelligent manufacturing solutions and seeking cooperation with factories to build new plants in a bid to commercialize the technology as soon as possible. China Mobile 5G Joint Innovation Center proposed a 5G intelligent factory solution, which involves five scenarios (industrial automatic control, personnel operation interaction, material supply management, equipment testing management, and environmental testing management), three major slices (industrial control slice, industrial multimedia slice, and industrial IoT slice), and three clouds (edge cloud, core cloud, and remote cloud). China Unicom and COMAC have built Shanghai Aircraft Manufacturing Co., Ltd. into a 5G smart factory. A safe and reliable 5G network environment ensures the full connectivity of the numerically controlled workshop and the full life-cycle control of composite materials as well as the quick comparison of on-site image data with cloud DigiFax by industrial dual cameras and AR remote equipment inspection and maintenance, indicating that the application of 5G in industrial scenarios is starting to produce results.

China's top enterprises responsible for the commercialization of 5G+ intelligent manufacturing technology have also made significant achievements in terms of applying 5G technology to industrial production. As the Fourth Industrial Revolution started and rapidly advanced on a global scale, China's "Lighthouse Network" already started to commercialize 5G+ intelligent manufacturing technologies. The "Lighthouse Network" refers to the factories that lead the way in contributing to the large-scale adoption of Fourth Industrial Revolution technologies. The World Economic Forum identified 16 out of more than 1,000 advanced manufacturers as "Lighthouses". China's Foxconn and Haier are included. Foxconn made predictions by using Industrial AI and put forward the idea of Fog AI. Fog AI is a smart control system placed closer to the terminal equipment. The system is able to process data more quickly, safely and intelligently, effectively avoid information delay, and build important data models and decision-making mechanisms at the edge. Haier has integrated AI + 5G technology into the entire process to create more than 200 new user experience models such as second-level response on the cloud, VR roaming, and intelligent coordination and facilitated the upgrade of the user-centered mass customization model. Moreover, Haier has supported interconnected factories with 136 AI + 5G technologies and built an innovation system featuring cross-border integration, ecological win–win, and technological iteration to realize multi-scenario high-end manufacturing and contribute to total factor decision-making by the interconnected factories themselves.

Intelligent manufacturing and 5G are clear directions for the development of the industrial and information network fields. In terms of the amount of information and information transfer efficiency, 5G fully meets intelligent manufacturing requirements, and intelligent factories and industrial Internet are the important foundation in the initial stage of 5G's across-the-board application. The complementarity between 5G and intelligent manufacturing gave a strong boost to the revolutionary upgrading of the industrial and information network fields.

Chapter 4

The Application of Intelligent Mass Production Based on 5G: Overcoming the Obstacles of Intelligent Production

According to the introduction in Chapter 3, 5G technology will be applied in smart manufacturing in a more extensive and in-depth manner. The overall architecture of 5G+ smart manufacturing mainly includes the following four layers: data layer, network layer, platform layer, and application layer. How is 5G technology applied in intelligent manufacturing in actual production and manufacturing? With a combination of physical products and cases, this chapter introduces more thoroughly the key technologies and typical applications of 5G+ intelligent manufacturing.

4.1 Application of Information Physical System Based on 5G

In recent years, computing technology, communication technology, and control technology have seen rapid development and application, and IT application, automation, intelligence, and industrial manufacturing have been further integrated. The traditional precise point technology can no longer satisfy the IT application and networking of the new generation of production equipment. Against this background, the cyber-physical system emerged. The previous chapters also noted that CPS is the foundation of the Fourth Industrial Revolution and the nature of intelligent manufacturing.

CPS can realize intelligence through the following four models:

(1) *Perceptual design*: The autonomous perception of information in the system environment relies on the wide application of various sensors.
(2) *Information processing*: The data collected by sensors are analyzed and processed, such as data presenting, classifying, and storing.
(3) *Modeling and cognition*: A database is established to model the system for more in-depth cognition and mining.
(4) *Decision and control*: Through data and model analysis, artificial intelligence, Big Data analysis, and other technologies are applied to improve the system's decision-making, control methods, and manufacturing efficiency.

CPS is mostly applied in the following areas in the field of intelligent manufacturing: the access to a massive number of sensors in factories, industrial cloud platforms, industrial digital transformation, etc.

4.1.1 *The access of massive number of sensors to factories*

4.1.1.1 *What is a sensor?*

Like a human's sensory systems (e.g., eyes, ears, and nose), a sensor is a detector that detects light, heat, movement, moisture, pressure, and other information and converts the detected information into electrical signals or other needed forms of information according to certain rules to realize the transmission, processing, storage, display, recording, and control of information.

The application of sensors offers objects sense organs such as touch, taste, and smell, "enlivening" the objects. Based on basic sensing functions, sensors can be divided into 10 categories: photosensor, thermal sensor, force sensor, gas sensor, humidity sensor, magneto sensor, radiation sensor, acoustic sensor, color sensor, and taste sensor.

Sensors are the key to realizing automatic detection and control, and intelligent manufacturing starts with sensors. Sensors are nothing new as they have been used for a very long time. The first sensor was invented in the 19th century. However, with the development of intelligent manufacturing and IoT, sensors have been more widely used with much more functions. For example, the intelligent driving car has become the focus of development in recent years, and the realization of its features depends on numerous sensor devices, such as cameras, millimeter wave radar, and lidar (Fig. 4.1).

A key part of intelligent manufacturing is intelligent monitoring, including real-time parameter acquisition, production equipment monitoring, production line process monitoring, and material consumption monitoring. The monitoring will be realized with the use of a large number of sensor devices. The massive access to sensors further strains the traditional wired signal transmission. The development and application of 5G networks enable the transition to wireless transmission, i.e., wireless sensor network technology.

Wireless sensor network technology is a new type of information acquisition and processing technology. It applies the same standard, i.e., 802.15.14 as that of wireless network technology. A wireless sensor network system (WSNS) is composed of sensor nodes, cluster nodes, and management nodes. The wireless sensor networks integrate sensor

Figure 4.1 Sensor configuration in an intelligent driving vehicle.

50 *The World of 5G: Intelligent Manufacturing*

technology, communication technology, embedded computing technology, distributed information processing technology, etc., and can monitor, sense, and collect information on different monitoring objects in the network distribution area in a real-time and collaborative manner.

The keys to industrial wireless sensor networks are low-power sensor nodes, network routers (with mesh network routing features), and wireless gateways (transmitting information to industrial Ethernet and control center or networking through transmission on the Internet). The 5G network with high speed, low-latency, and wide-range connection will become their essential supporting technology.

4.1.1.2 *Different types of sensors*

There are various types of industrial sensors, with demanding performance indicators. In terms of features, industrial sensors can be divided into the following categories:

(1) *Temperature sensor*: As the core of the temperature measurement instrument, various types of temperature sensors detect temperatures and convert them into usable output signals. The sensors can be divided into contact temperature sensors and non-contact ones based on different measurement methods and thermal resistance sensors and thermocouple ones based on the characteristics of materials and electronic components. Temperature sensors are widely used in intelligent manufacturing, such as the thermal state detection of materials and machines and the constant temperature control of manufacturing environments, working environments, and experimental environments.

(2) *Photoelectric sensor*: The photoelectric sensor converts light signals into electrical signals, and its working principle is based on the photoelectric effect. The photoelectric effect can be divided into the following three categories based on its different phenomena: external photoelectric effect, internal photoelectric effect, and photovoltaic effect. Photoelectric sensors are mostly used in product counting, barcode scanning, smoke turbidity detection, rotation speed measurement, etc.

(3) *Force/torque sensor*: Force sensors detect mechanical variables including tension, pressure, weight, torque, internal stress, and strain and convert them into electrical signals. Specific devices include

metal strain gauges, pressure sensors, etc. It is a core component that is integral to power equipment, engineering machinery, various types of machine tools, and industrial automation systems. Torque sensors convert the physical changes of torsion into accurate electrical signals. Torque sensors can be applied to make viscometers and electric (pneumatic and hydraulic) torque wrenches with high precision, fast frequency response, high-reliability, and long life.

(4) *Humidity sensor*: A humidity sensor detects humidity and converts it into an electrical signal. There are mainly two types of humidity sensors: resistive ones and capacitive ones. Humidity sensors were, in the first place, used in reports and weather forecasts in weather stations, and they are now widely used in industry, agriculture, environmental monitoring, food supply chain, HVAC, health monitoring, and many other aspects.

(5) *Sound and noise sensor*: A sound and noise sensor receives sound waves, displays the images of sound vibration, and monitors the noise level in the environment. Sound and noise sensors can measure noise and provide data to help prevent noise pollution. They are more valued in the fields of smart manufacturing and smart city construction.

(6) *Water level (liquid level) sensor*: A water level sensor, a pressure sensor that measures the liquid level, converts the water level parameter of the measured spot into a corresponding electric signal in real time. Such sensors are used in flood warning and have also been increasingly applied in various industrial fields to control and optimize manufacturing processes.

(7) *Presence and proximity sensor*: By emitting electromagnetic radiation beams, such sensors can sense the presence of the target object, identify the distance between the two and convert it into electrical signals for output. With their high-reliability and long life, presence and proximity sensors are widely applied in intelligent manufacturing fields, such as intelligent cars, robots, manufacturing, machinery, aviation, and even smart parking solutions.

(8) *Motion control sensor*: Motion control sensors convert non-electric changes such as speed and acceleration into electric ones such as displacement sensors, speed sensors, rotation speed sensors, and acceleration sensors. They are now widely used in parts production, automobile manufacturing, automatic production lines, and many other fields of intelligent manufacturing. Cars are generally equipped with multiple kinds of motion control sensors, as shown in Fig. 4.2.

52 *The World of 5G: Intelligent Manufacturing*

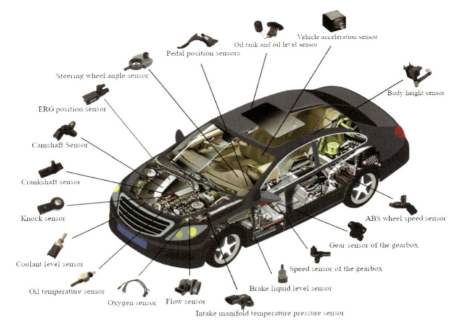

Figure 4.2 Vehicle sensors.

(9) *Chemical sensor*: Similar to people's sensory organs such as smell and taste, chemical sensors detect chemical substances (solid, liquid and gas) and convert their concentrations into electrical signals. They are widely used in industrial safety systems, environmental protection, scientific research, and other fields.

(10) *Image/vision sensor*: The image/vision sensor converts optical data into electrical pulses and detects information in the surrounding environment. The image/vision sensor can realize its features by using the laser scanner, linear array, and area array CCD (charge-coupled device) camera or TV camera, as well as the latest digital camera. Image/vision sensors are widely used in smart manufacturing fields such as mobile robots, intelligent vehicles, security systems, and medical imaging equipment.

(11) *Other sensors*: There are many other sensors in the market that are applied in different fields. These include tactile sensors, radiofrequency identification sensors, sonar sensors, ultrasonic sensors, radar sensors, and lidar sensors.

4.1.1.3 *Sensor market*

Major manufacturers in the global sensor market include Siemens (Siemens AG, Germany), Bosch, STMicroelectronics NV, Honeywell International, ABB, HBM, etc., as shown in Table 4.1.

Table 4.1 Major manufacturers and their product types and competitive areas in the global sensor market.

Major manufacturers	Product types	Competitive areas
Honeywell International	Pressure, temperature, humidity, infrared, ultrasonic waves, magnetic resistance, Hall, electric current, and other sensors	Aerospace, transportation, medicine, etc.
STMicroelectronics NV	Pressure sensor, acceleration sensor, MEMS radiofrequency devices, gyroscopes, etc.	Industrial control, automotive, medical electronics, consumer electronics, communications, and computers
Freescale	Acceleration, pressure. and other sensors	Automotive, consumer electronics, etc.
Bosch	Pressure, acceleration, gas and other sensors, as well as gyroscope	Automotive, consumer electronics, etc., and the world's largest MEMS sensor manufacturer
PCB	Acceleration, pressure, force, torque, and other sensors	Aerospace, shipping, weapons, nuclear industry, water conservancy, electricity, light industry, and transportation
ABB	Capacitive, current, inductive, photoelectric, ultrasonic, voltage, and other sensors	Aerospace, automobile, shipping, water conservancy, and light industry
HBM	Force, torque, displacement, strain type weighing, and other sensors	Aerospace, automobile, shipping, etc.
MEAS	Pressure, displacement, angular displacement, Hall, magnetic resistance, acceleration, vibration, humidity, temperature, infrared, photoelectric, piezoelectric film, and other sensors	Aerospace, machinery equipment, industrial automatic control, automobile, air conditioning, medicine, petrochemical industry, etc.
Philips	Weighing, temperature, and other sensors	Automobile, shipping, etc.

4.1.2 *Industrial cloud platform*

The sensor was introduced briefly in the previous section. After the sensor detected the target, how to process, analyze, and apply the detected data is at the heart of the intelligent manufacturing system. With the advancement of industrial electrification, automation, and intelligence, the data processing and analysis modules have grown to be cloud platforms from electronic control units.

4.1.2.1 *Wireless transmission network*

Data is at the core of the industrial cloud platform as the data collected from the sensors have to be received in real time for processing, analysis, and output to actuators, display interfaces, etc. This cannot be done without a data transmission network. With the development of industrial electrification, automation, and intelligence in the manufacturing industry, the number and types of sensors have multiplied, with an increasingly diversified data collection. In particular, intelligence has raised more demanding requirements for the speed and reliability of data transmission. The traditional wired transmission will mean limitations for wire layout, hardware interface, etc. The transmission has to go from wired to wireless.

A wireless network can be connected through cellular mobile communications, low-power wide-area network (LPWAN), Bluetooth and Wi-Fi, and so on. Following modes of connection, which people use in daily life, are widely used in smart manufacturing and the IoT:

(1) *Cellular mobile communications*: The term may sound unfamiliar, but in fact, all of us have been benefiting from cellular mobile communications as our mobile phones use it to send and receive data. It also represents the familiar 2G, 3G, 4G, and other networks.
(2) *Low-power wide-area network (LPWAN)*: Like LoRa and Sigfox, the LPWAN network is relatively new, and only a few countries are entitled to its application nationwide. According to McKinsey & Company, LPWAN is available to 20% of the world's population by 2017. As its name suggests, LPWAN has two important characteristics: low-power consumption (using small batteries with several years of battery life) and long-distance communication (in kilometers). LPWAN technology is based on the concept of intermittently sending a small amount of data (e.g., data may be sent only a few times a day)

to enable low-power consumption. However, its applications in automation and intelligence are very limited.

(3) *Bluetooth and Wi-Fi*: Bluetooth and Wi-Fi are the best options for short-distance communication. Its cellular mobile network involves low-power consumption and has a higher bandwidth and transmission frequency than that of LPWAN.

Coverage, bandwidth, power consumption, cost, reliability, availability, and many other aspects have to be taken into consideration in selecting wireless networks. The optimal network connection has many characteristics such as wide range connection, high speed, low cost, and low-power consumption. Unfortunately, such a connection technology is not available so far. Wider coverage tends to increase power consumption, while increased bandwidth usually means growing costs. One of the solutions is to use multiple wireless networks at the same time to satisfy various demands; another solution is to develop new network technologies, such as Narrowband Internet of Things (NB-IoT), an LPWAN technology that uses the existing cellular network infrastructure.

4.1.2.2 *The basic architecture of the industrial cloud platform*

The industrial cloud platform is a cloud platform that is geared to the digital, networked, and intelligent needs of the manufacturing industry, builds a service system based on massive data collection, aggregation, and analysis, and supports the ubiquitous connection, flexible supply, and efficient allocation of the manufacturing resources. The platform has three core layers: edge, platform (industrial PaaS), and application, and its basic architecture is shown in Fig. 4.3.

The first layer is the edge layer, which lays the data foundation of the industrial Internet platform through a large-scale and in-depth data collection and the protocol conversion and edge processing of the heterogeneous data. The second layer is the platform layer. Based on the common PaaS overlapped by innovative functions such as Big Data processing, industrial data analysis, and industrial micro services, this layer built an extensible open cloud operating system. The third layer is the application layer, which forms industrial SaaS and apps that cater to different industries and scenarios, demonstrating the ultimate value of the industrial Internet platform. The industrial Internet platform also includes IaaS infrastructure and a safety management system, covering the entire

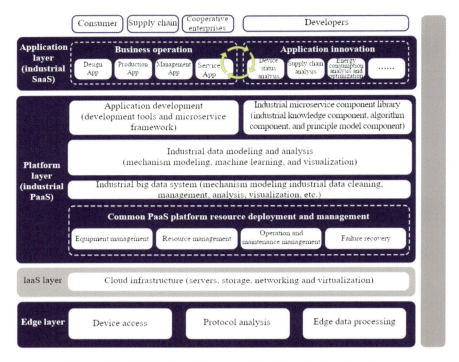

Figure 4.3 The basic architecture of the industrial cloud platform.

industrial system. Together, they provide the basic support and important guarantee of the industrial Internet platform.

Figures 4.4 and 4.5 show typical application cases of two industrial cloud platforms.

Ubiquitous connection, cloud-based services, the accumulation of knowledge, and application innovation are the four characteristics of the industrial cloud platform. These can be described as follows: (1) ubiquitous connection refers to the ability to comprehensively collect data of all factors of production, including equipment, software, and personnel; (2) cloud-based services realize the massive data storage, management, and calculation based on cloud computing architecture; (3) the accumulation of knowledge provides data analysis capabilities based on industrial knowledge mechanisms and realizes the storage, accumulation, and reuse of knowledge; (4) application innovation uses the features and resources on the platform to provide an open industrial app development environment for the innovative applications of the industrial app.

The Application of Intelligent Mass Production Based on 5G 57

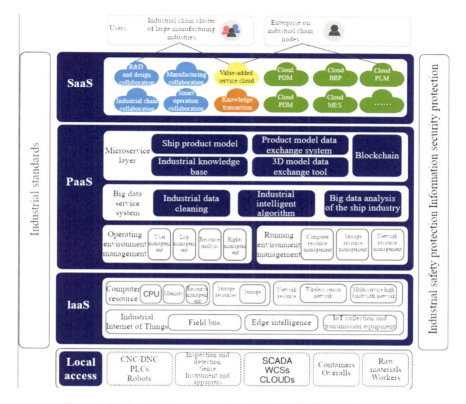

Figure 4.4 The intelligent operation platform of CSIC industrial ship.

4.1.2.3 *The core technologies of the industrial cloud platform*

The industrial cloud platform has to address a series of problems, including multi-type industrial equipment access, multi-source industrial data integration, massive data management and processing, industrial data modeling and analysis, the innovation and integration of industrial applications, and the accumulation and iteration of industrial knowledge. The solutions to these problems involve seven categories of key technologies, as shown in Fig. 4.6.

These can be described as follows:

(1) Data integration and edge processing technology, including equipment access (industrial bus, Ethernet, optical fiber and other

58 *The World of 5G: Intelligent Manufacturing*

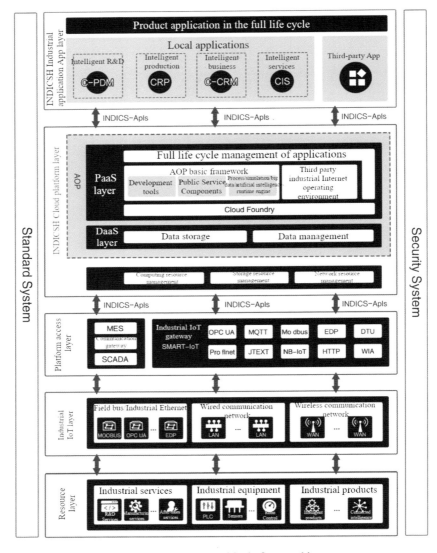

Figure 4.5 CASIC INDICS platform architecture.

communication protocols as well as 3G/4G/5G, NB-IoT and other wireless protocols), protocol conversion (protocol analysis, format conversion and remote transmission), edge data processing, and other technologies.

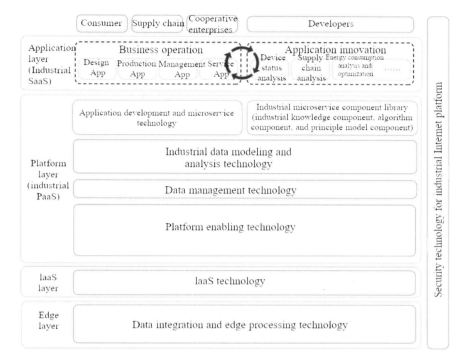

Figure 4.6 The key technology system of the industrial cloud platform.

(2) IaaS technology, based on virtualization, distributed storage, parallel computing, load balancing, and other technologies, realizes the pooled management of computer resources such as network, computing, and storage allocates flexibly on the basis of different needs and ensures the safe and isolated use of resources to offer users perfect cloud infrastructure services.

(3) Platform enabling technology monitors the dynamic changes in the business volume of cloud applications in real time for reasonable resource scheduling and protects different users' privacy and security with respective applications and services through virtualization, database isolation, sandbox, and other technologies.

(4) Data management technologies include data processing framework (e.g., distributed processing architecture and massive data batch processing and stream processing computing requirements), data preprocessing (e.g., the use of data redundancy elimination, anomaly detection, normalization, and other methods to clean the original

data), data storage and management (e.g., the partition selection, storage, cataloging, and indexing of tons of industrial data), and other technologies.

(5) Industrial data modeling and analysis technologies include data analysis algorithms (e.g., mathematical statistics, machine learning, artificial intelligence, and other applications of algorithms), mechanism modeling (e.g., physical models and simulation models), and other technologies.

(6) Application development and micro-service technologies include multi-language and tool support (e.g., Java, Ruby, PHP, and other multi-language compiling and translating environments, Eclipse Integration, JBoss Developer Studio, Jenkins, and various types of development tools), micro-service architecture (the management mechanism and operating environment of service registration, discovery, communication, and invocation), graphical programming, and other technologies.

(7) Technologies that ensure the safety of industrial Internet platforms include data access security, platform security, access security, and information security.

4.1.2.4 *The industrial ecology of the industrial cloud platform*

The industrial cloud platform industry involves multiple levels and fields, as shown in Fig. 4.7. In the upper reaches of the industrial chain, five types of enterprises specialized in professional and technical services such as cloud computing, data management, data analysis, data acquisition and integration, and network and edge computing provide technical support for the building of the platform; in the middle reaches of the industrial chain, top companies in the four major areas of equipment and automation, information and communication technology, industrial software, and manufacturing are stepping up efforts to shape the platform; in the lower reaches of the industrial chain, vertical field users and third-party developers continue to add new value into the platform through application deployment and innovation.

(1) *Information technology enterprises*: Such enterprises provide key technical capabilities and help build the platform in an "integrated" manner. These mainly include five types of enterprises: cloud computing enterprises, data management enterprises, data analysis enterprises, data acquisition and integration enterprises, and network and edge

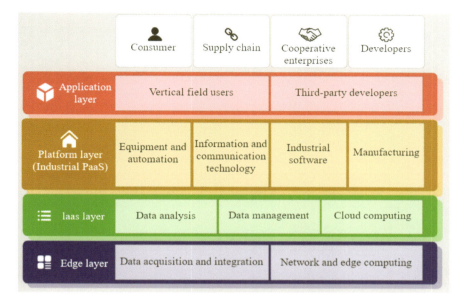

Figure 4.7 The industrial cloud platform industrial system.

computing enterprises. They offer universal enabling tools and critical support for platform building.

(2) *Platform enterprises*: Integrated innovation is the main model of such enterprises, which aim at the application of innovative ecological construction. Integrating various industrial and technical elements for platform building lies at the heart of the industrial system. Platform enterprises mainly include four types of enterprises: equipment and automation enterprises, information and communication technology enterprises, manufacturing enterprises, and industrial software enterprises. Such enterprises build the platform through resource integration and lead the industry.

(3) *Subjects of application*: The industrial cloud platform massively lowers the threshold of industrial application and innovation through making features public and mobilizing resources. More subjects are applying intelligent manufacturing with its further development. They mainly include vertical field users and third-party developers, who undertake application and innovation on the platform and raise the value of the platform.

4.1.3 *Industrial digital transformation*

4.1.3.1 *Digital transformation*

As automation and intelligence are more frequently applied at all levels and in all stages in industrial manufacturing, sensors and cloud platforms are more widely applied. The transition will be made from the application in a single device and scene to that in a complete production system and management process and finally to the overall interconnection of the collaborative organization of industrial resources. The data will be further analyzed, turning from the descriptive analysis featuring visualization to rule-based diagnostic analysis, predictive analysis based on mining and modeling, and guiding analysis based on deep learning as industrial manufacturing is going digital, as shown in Fig. 4.8.

(1) Single scenarios such as equipment and processes are entering the decisive analysis stage. With the extensive application of sensors, devices, equipment, products, etc., are widely connected to the industrial cloud. Equipment mechanism models and product data mining enable a massive number of single-point applications, including rule-based fault diagnosis, process parameter optimization, equipment

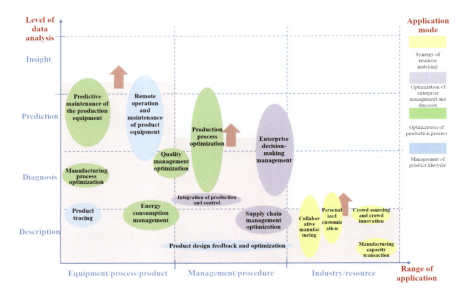

Figure 4.8   The digital application of industrial manufacturing.

status trend prediction, and component life prediction. For example, on the Predix platform, GE realized the health management of heavy equipment such as aero engines and gas turbines through building digital twins. Based on the EcoStruxure platform, Schneider provides power distribution equipment management services for the Rochester Medical Center and realizes predictive alarm and analysis of power failures. With more data and improved analysis methods, a more accurate analysis model based on product data mining will be established, and constructive suggestions for optimization will be independently proposed. The trend has already manifested itself. For example, the Microsoft Azure IoT platform provides Rolls-Royce engines with machine learning-based massive data analysis and model construction, enabling accurate prediction of abnormalities and intervention in advance before component failures to help Rolls-Royce with solution planning.

(2) Enterprise management and process optimization are advancing from partial improvement to systematic global optimization. The industrial cloud platform realizes the coordination and unification of the production site with enterprise operation management and the scheduling of resources, which made key applications of production process optimization, enterprise intelligent management, and supply chain management optimization for part of the enterprise possible. Hitachi's Lumada platform collects commodity circulation data in real time through IoT equipment and forms a huge supply chain management data pool by interconnection with the subsidiary's truck deployment business system, in a bid to realize the optimization of the warehouse logistics across the group. Moving forward, with the improvement of the platform's underlying connection capabilities and the availability of the enterprises' information technology (IT) and the operational technology (OT) layer, tons of production site data and management system data will be integrated. With massive data analysis and mining, the overall optimization of smart factories, enterprises' real-time intelligent decision-making, as well as the systematic improvement of the enterprises' production management sectors will be realized. Rockwell Automation's automation department cooperated with Microsoft's Azure platform to get access to the data of the automation system in the OT layer and the business system in the IT layer. With large volumes of data, factory system modeling and correlation analysis can be carried out, and production material management, product

quality inspection, the integration of production, management and control, as well as other comprehensive functions can be realized to explore the application of the digital factory.

(3) In the industry/resource layer, information interaction will evolve to the optimized allocation of resources. The industrial cloud platform gathers a large amount of industrial data, model algorithms, software tools, R&D, design, production and processing, and various other resources in the application process. Currently, these resources realized a superficial level of applications such as supply–demand matching and resource sharing on the platform through information exchange. In the future, with the gradual improvement of the platform's overall operation and analysis and the system's modeling capabilities, the platform will serve as a key carrier for the optimal allocation of global resources. For instance, in addition to providing steel resource supply–demand matching services for enterprises in the upper and lower reaches of the steel industry, zhaogang.com is exploring precise supply–demand matching of steel mills based on Big Data analysis, regional optimization and distribution of resources, and optimal pricing strategies.

4.1.3.2 *Industrial digital application*

(1) *Production process optimization on the industrial site*: With the extensive application of sensors, the industrial cloud platform can effectively collect and aggregate production site data, such as equipment operation data, process parameters, quality inspection data, material distribution data, and schedule management data, which will be optimized in the manufacturing processes, production processes, quality management, equipment maintenance, energy consumption management, and other specific application scenarios through data analysis and feedback.

For example, in terms of manufacturing process optimization, based on the Predix platform (Fig. 4.9), GE optimizes the drilling technique parameters of high-pressure turbine blades and increases the product's one-time molding rate to more than 95% from lower than 25%. When it comes to production process optimization, based on the industrial cloud platform, Bosch provides OSRAM with production performance management services, which can coordinate data from different sources in the production environment, extract

Figure 4.9 The architecture of the Predix platform.

valuable information, and automatically use expert databases to evaluate and realize the automatic allocation of production tasks.

In terms of quality management optimization, the Foxconn Group realizes automatic diagnosis of the yield of all its products on its platform, gets access to all kinds of operation status data such as workshop capacity, quality, manpower, and cost, and analyzes and calculates related data and optimizes Big Data to save 90% of the time needed for yield diagnosis. In terms of equipment maintenance and optimization, based on the Intel IoT platform's intelligent gateway and monitoring technologies, Kontron sends machine operation data and fault parameters to the background system for modeling and analysis and realizes the predictive maintenance of board manufacturing equipment. While Schneider provides EcoStruxure energy efficiency management platform services for the Comira silicomanganese and electrolytic manganese smelting plants in energy consumption management optimization and establishes a unified architecture that integrates functions such as energy equipment management, production energy consumption analysis, and energy event management to realize energy consumption optimization in the manganese ore production process.

(2) *Management decision-making optimization for enterprise operation*: With the industrial cloud platform, data of the production site, enterprise management, and supply chain will be available, and decision-making efficiency will be improved for more accurate and transparent enterprise management. Specific application scenarios include supply chain management optimization, the integration of production, management and control, and enterprise decision-making management.

66 *The World of 5G: Intelligent Manufacturing*

For example, the Bluemix platform of IBM (International Business Machines Corporation) extracted and conducted a multi-dimensional analysis of important data in the supply chain and production system. On this basis, Youngor optimized its supply chain management and more than doubled inventory turnover, saving 250 million yuan of inventory cost, reducing more than 30% of shortage costs and 99% of the factory's products could be delivered on time. In terms of the integration of production, management and control, with the help of the ProMACE platform (Fig. 4.10) and a focus on the optimization of production plans, PCITC promoted performance analysis, the integrated coordination of supply chain and production scheduling, as well as the closed-loop control of real-time optimization, advanced control, and control loop to realize the daily or monthly financial settlement. With a combination of the computing power of the SAP HANA platform and SAP SLT data replication technologies, in terms of enterprise decision-making management, Zoomlion realized real-time analysis in three areas: engineering crane sales services, customer credit sales, and the group's internal control and operation, which enables effective, quick, and intelligent decision-making in response to market changes.

(3) *Optimal allocation and coordination of resources for socialized production*: The industrial cloud platform facilitates the realization of the

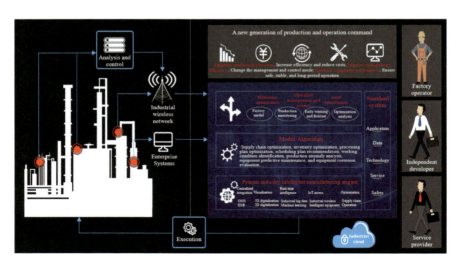

Figure 4.10   ProMACE platform architecture.

all-round connection between manufacturing enterprises and external user requirements, innovation resources, and production capacities and promotes the parallel organization and collaborative optimization of design, manufacturing, supply, and services. Specific scenarios include collaborative manufacturing, manufacturing capacity trading, and personalized customization.

For example, in terms of collaborative manufacturing, Henan Aerospace Pressure Components Co., Ltd. realized collaborative R&D and process design with the overall design department and final assembly plants and institutions on the INDICS platform, shortening the R&D cycle by 35% and increasing the resource utilization rate by 30% and production efficiency by 40%. In terms of manufacturing capacity transaction optimization, Shenyang Machine Tool Co., Ltd. (SMTCL) provided i5 machine tool leasing services to Aobang Forging Company on the iSESOL platform, and via this platform, SMTCL also provided machine tools to the company on a finance lease, and payment is based on the manufacturing capacity, effectively lowering user fund threshold and releasing production capacity. In terms of personalized customization, Haier interacts with users and tracks the entire process of users' personalized customization orders on the COSMOPlat platform (Fig. 4.11). Meanwhile, requirements collection, product orders, raw

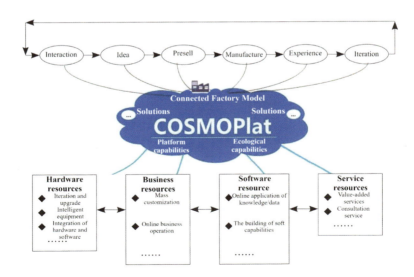

Figure 4.11   COSMOPlat architecture.

68   *The World of 5G: Intelligent Manufacturing*

material supply, product design, production assembly, and intelligent analysis will be available to set up a production system that caters to the mass customization model and produces more than 6,000 personalized customization plans, which will increase the percentage of pass by 2% and shorten the delivery cycle by 50%. In terms of industry–finance integration, RootCloud and Long Insurance jointly launched the UBI (usage-based insurance) data platform for excavator warranty extension products based on RootCloud, identifying machine types fit for the business and guiding insurances' precise pricing of every business.

(4) *Management and service optimization for the entire life cycle of the product*: The industrial cloud platform is able to fully integrate product design, production, operation, and service data. Based on the traceability of the whole life cycle, the platform realizes manufacturability prediction in design and health management in utilization. Moreover, it improves product design through the feedback from data production and utilization. At present, its specific application scenarios include product traceability, product/equipment remote predictive maintenance, and product design feedback and optimization.

For example, in terms of product traceability optimization, PTC adopts the full life cycle traceability system of the ThingWorx platform to help the chip manufacturer ATI (Array Technology Industry) realize the full accessibility from production to utilization, and each product is equipped with a single data source to provide comprehensive and accurate information in after-sales services; in remote predictive maintenance, SAP collects real-time data of various train components through sensor installation, and based on the HANA platform, real-time data and maintenance data and instruments and apparatus' parameters are collected and integrated for analysis to provide the Italian railway operator Trenitalia with a remote diagnosis of the train's operation status and predictive maintenance plans; in terms of product design feedback and optimization, GE adopts the Predix platform to optimize the design of its own engines. The platform first collects and analyzes the service data after the product delivery. Then, based on the analysis of a massive amount of accumulated data and feedback from airlines' operation information, the platform optimizes the model and parameters on the design end and processes and procedures on the manufacturing end. It also improves the design and enhances the performance of the engine through iterations.

4.2 5G-Driven Industrial AR/VR Applications

4.2.1 *Super flexible deployment and upgrade of AR/VR-assisted intelligent manufacturing*

A lot of people say that 3G made WeChat and 4G made video. Now that 5G is here, what will the next achievement be? Would it be augmented reality/virtual reality, manless driving, or industrial Internet? In fact, with the arrival of 5G, the biggest impact is on the telecom operators. At present, challenges of 5G to the operators are mainly reflected in the following aspects:

1. *Conflict between limited time and heavy task*: 5G went from standard to commercial deployment in less than a year, while 4G took five years. From the perspective of scenarios, 5G is more diversified with more diversified deployments. The 5G core network is also a brand new architecture, so the time is tight and the task is heavy.
2. *Conflict between maturity and high expectations*: Governments at all levels and many enterprises have high expectations for 5G. But in fact, it will take a long time for 5G to be standardized, applied in the whole industry and mature in the entire industry terminal.
3. *Conflict between investment and income*: The cost of 5G base station and power consumption is 3.5–4 times that of 4G. Besides, 5G has a high-frequency band and wider coverage, so the whole investment is very large. Meanwhile, the business model is not clear yet, so the operators face great pressure.
4. *Contradiction of limited resources*: With the launch of products and services such as non-zero clearing package and unlimited package, the traffic used by users is surging, and there is a need for further cooperation and communication between different operators.

The impact of 5G on the industry can be divided into three categories: (1) it brings about industry mutations, such as mobile surveillance, high-definition video, and AR/VR; (2) it helps further optimize industries, such as healthcare and education; (3) it brings more innovation to some industries, such as energy, manufacturing, and car networking. At present, the industrial field urgently needs to build a new generation of wireless communication. The existing wireless communication protocols are numerous, inadequate, and relatively closed, which makes it difficult to interconnect devices and restricts the uploading of information from devices to the cloud platform. 5G can realize the mechanization, cost reduction and increase efficiency; it can replace fixed devices with mobile devices and support flexible manufacturing; electro-mechanical disassociation can be realized to achieve rapid iteration of equipment. Specific application scenarios include machine vision, industrial welding, remote field, and remote control. The application of 5G is actually a phased maturation process. Currently, 5G will be the first to be applied in AR/VR and HD video fields, as the enhanced mobile broadband (eMBB) standard is the first to mature. With the advance of other network standards, low delay and high speed will be popular, but overall, it is still in the stage of gradual development.

4.2.2 *Definition and overview of virtual reality*

Virtual reality technology, also known as artificial environment, is the use of computers or other intelligent computing equipment to create a three-dimensional virtual world and to provide users with visual, auditory, tactile, and other sensory simulation experience. The VR industry covers hardware, systems, platforms, development tools, applications, and consumer content.

At present, the virtual reality industry is in the initial growth stage. Local governments in China are actively issuing special policies, and local industry development has its own characteristics. At the present stage, the ecology of China's virtual reality industry has initially taken shape, and the industry chain mainly involves subdivided fields, such as content application, terminal devices, network communication/platform, and content production system.

VR technology is booming around the world. Technology giants such as Google, Sony, and Facebook have stepped up research and development of related technologies and products, and a number of domestic companies have also launched VR products.

Intelligent wearable devices refer to intelligent devices that are developed and designed by applying advanced electronic technology to daily wearable devices. VR products can be mainly divided into mobile VR, PC VR, and VR all-in-one machines, as shown in Table 4.2.

The arrival of 5G is a key push for AR/VR to usher in its spring. At present, it is difficult for users to experience smooth VR videos at the transmission speed of the 4G network. For AR experience, when a large

Table 4.2 VR classification and related products.

Type	Mobile VR	PC VR	All-in-one VR
Characteristics	The price is low, they're easy to popularize, and the content is mainly 3D mobile game and video	Mainstream VR products are relatively mature, with good user experience and rich content	Good portability
Representative products	Storm Mirror, Xiaomi VR, Ling VR MK, and Dream VR	3GClass, ANTVR, Game Madman, and EMAX	Qualcomm VR820, Wondergate VR, and Deepoon VR
Potential applications	Mobile Internet light application video, mobile game, audio and video, social networking, etc.	Deep gamers and audio–visual users	Daily application, professional office work, deep video, and audio games

number of dynamic changes occur in the recognized scene, it is difficult to rely on the terminal alone to load a huge amount of computation. In the 5G era, a large amount of processing can be carried out on the cloud through cloud computing. Such processing with high CPU/GPU will not produce excessive power consumption, and it can be quickly transmitted to the local area through the fast connection of 5G, which will strongly support the improvement of the AR/VR product experience of users. 5G uses a much higher frequency than 4G networks and the higher the frequency, the wider the spectrum. Broadening the frequency band can greatly improve the transmission amount per unit time and then bring the transmission rate to an ultra-high speed. For example, Huawei VR OpenLab, together with other partners such as Cyber Cloud, released the latest VR solution — Cloud VR at MWC (Mobile World Congress) in Spain, which is to transfer VR operation capability from terminal to cloud, in order to promote the popularization of VR/AR applications in smartphones.

In terms of the construction of the 5G base station, compared with the macro sites built for the 4G network, most of the base stations used by the 5G network are miniature base stations. 5G uses mobile edge computing, in which processing logic sinks to the edge of the network or base stations closer to the user. Once the user requests it, the data can be sent to the base

72 The World of 5G: Intelligent Manufacturing

station in a very short time, and the base station can respond to the user more quickly. Therefore, the 5G network can greatly shorten the time delay of AR/VR applications in mobile terminals.

According to IDC's latest top 10 predictions for the AR/VR market in 2019, the AR/VR industry applications are further expanded and deepened, and the subdivision of the consumption scene has been constantly enriched. First of all, the market for all-in-one movie-watching VR will continue to expand, and home IMAX movie watching is expected to lead the development of the global VR market. Secondly, the application of AR technology plays an important role in the intelligent development of industrial Internet. Visual control is realized through the combination of IoT and AR technology, and AR/VR will be further expanded in mobile terminals, games, social networking, marketing, e-commerce, and other fields. For traditional AR/VR games, due to the low user penetration rate at present, with the increase of domestic manufacturers' investment, it is expected to further improve its market space in the future.

At present, very few listed companies do business involving the AR/VR integration, but enterprises in the industry chain can share this cake. The hardware mainly includes chips, sensors, and display devices, and the software can be divided into basic software and application software. The storage industry chain includes GigaDevice, the chip industry chain includes Ingenic and Allwinner Technology, the CMOS (Collection Objectives Management System) vendors include OV (Will), including Sunny Optical Technology (Group) Co. Ltd., O-film, Union, LCE, Lite-On (Luxshare), Nanyang Lida Optic-electronics Co. Ltd., Crystal Optic-electronics, CASTECH INC., NOVEL, Goertek (AR OEM), Shenzhen Lianchuang Circuit Co., Ltd., and the overall solution includes Leyard and others.

4.2.3 Industrial wearables and flexible deployment of industrial image processing

The development of the manufacturing industry is inseparable from the progress of science and technology. From 1978 to 1987, China's manufacturing industry was in its initial stage, and the small- and medium-sized enterprises were mainly managed by individual efforts and manual work, which was relatively backward. From 1988 to 1997, China's manufacturing industry was in the growth stage, and private enterprises began to rise. At the same time, many foreign-funded enterprises entered China, and China's manufacturing industry developed rapidly. At this stage, they were mainly managed by departmental software. From 1998 to 2011, China's manufacturing industry was on the rise, Chinese enterprises began to integrate into the world, and Made in China became famous around the world. Since 2002, China has transformed itself from a manufacturer of quantity to a manufacturer of quality, with the transformation of Made in China to Create in China. China has implemented the Made in China 2025 Internet+ action plan to integrate mobile Internet, cloud computing, Big Data, and IoT with modern manufacturing. Internet+ is a major opportunity for China's economic transformation. Traditional industries have their own advantages, and we need to integrate them with Internet+ to unleash greater vitality. The essence of Internet+ is industrial Internet, which coincides with Industry 4.0. Internet+ is an upgraded version of the integration of informationization and industrialization. It will promote Made in China to Wisdom in China.

4.2.4 *Automatic transmission and data acquisition of factory information*

Through the seamless connection of the field intelligent terminal and ERP/MES (enterprise resource planning/production execution system), the production and operation information of the whole factory can be quickly, promptly, and automatically transmitted to any work station or machine equipment in the field of the factory. Through data acquisition, human–computer interaction, and machine–machine interconnection of the field intelligent terminal, the information can be promptly fed back to the data center so as to realize the timely circulation of information inside the factory. Traditional production methods use printed documents to convey production information and data. With the rise of low-batch, multi-variety production methods, it can take longer to compile, print, and distribute a work order document than it takes to complete the production of the work order. Small batch efficient manufacturing first requires efficient transmission of information and data, and the data collected by people and machines on the site can be transmitted to the MES server in time, and the information and data of MES can also be transmitted to people and machines on the production site in time. The field intelligent terminal perfectly plays the role of field data acquisition and efficient data transmission between man and machine MES.

Automatic information transmission and data acquisition based on VR/AR can help upgrade intelligent manufacturing to super flexible

74 *The World of 5G: Intelligent Manufacturing*

deployment. The super flexible deployment of intelligent manufacturing is mainly embodied in the organization, logistics, production, and other aspects.

4.2.4.1 *Super flexibility*

This can be assessed from three aspects: organization, logistics and production. Organizational flexibility includes collaborative planning, priority modeling, material occupancy. Production cooperation includes cross-factory process cooperation, cross-factory material receiving, cross-factory warehousing, cross-factory entrusted processing. Manufacturing strategy includes manufacturing to stock (MTS), manufacturing to order (MTO), manufacturing to order (ATO).

4.2.4.2 *Organizational flexibility*

(i) *Coordination between sales and production organizations*:
   A. *Centralized sales, decentralized production, and centralized delivery*: The Group takes orders uniformly, and all factories complete their own production. After the factories complete the production tasks, the products will be stored or transferred to the Group, and the Group will be responsible for delivering the products to the customers.
   B. *Centralized sales, decentralized production, and decentralized delivery*: The group takes orders uniformly, and all factories complete their own production. After the factories complete the production tasks, the products are delivered directly to the customers.
(ii) *Coordination of production planning between organizations*:
   A. The Group's unified plan shall be implemented by all factories. The Group shall compile MPS (Master Production Plan)/MRP (Material Requirements Plan) uniformly, and the factory shall only be responsible for the implementation of the plan.
   B. The Group prepares the product plan, each factory prepares MRP, the group uniformly weighs the factory capacity load, the Group uniformly distributes and plans product orders, and the factory prepares MPS/MRP according to the Group's product plan.

C. Inter-organizational collaborative planning in which all organizations independently prepare their plans and transmit the demands among organizations in the form of demand sheets.

(iii) *Coordination of purchasing plan between organizations*:

A. *Centralized planning, centralized procurement, and centralized receipt:* These involve unified management of material procurement by the Group, unified formulation of procurement plans by the Group, and fully integrated utilization of resources and reduction of waste.

B. *Decentralized planning, centralized purchasing, and decentralized receiving*: The Group shall formulate purchasing policies uniformly, the factory shall formulate purchasing plans, and the factory shall be responsible for purchasing and receiving goods.

(iv) *Coordination of production and execution between organizations*:

A. *Process coordination*: Some processes are processed by cooperative factories, and processing fees are settled between factories.

B. *Commissioned/entrusted cooperation*: The factory entrusts the products/parts to other factories for processing, the principal provides the raw materials, and the principal and the agent settle the processing costs.

C. *Material coordination*: Cross-organization material collection and cross-organization warehousing.

4.2.4.3 *Logistics flexibility*

Automatic transmission and timely delivery of materials in the factory: The process of smart material supply, code scanning drive of the whole logistics business, barcode rules, barcode generation, barcode printing, and barcode scanning is shown in Fig. 4.12.

4.2.4.4 *Production flexibility*

Cellular production unit: The former production mode has shortcomings like large quantities, rigid, complex switching of production lines, difficulty in responding to personalized and small batch market demand, and difficulty in meeting the requirements of today's production. The cellular production unit has the following advantages: single piece flow, more flexible and humanized, and high utilization rate of independent space.

76 *The World of 5G: Intelligent Manufacturing*

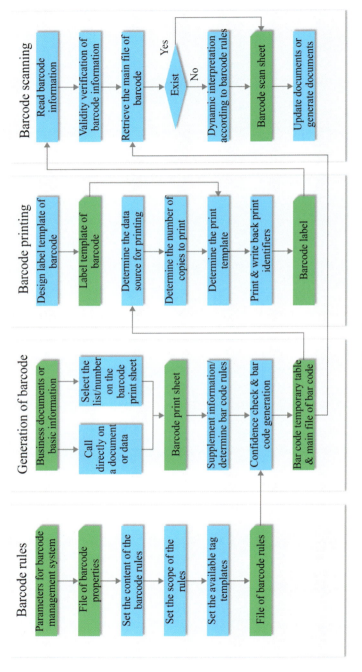

Figure 4.12 A flow chart of barcode scanning.

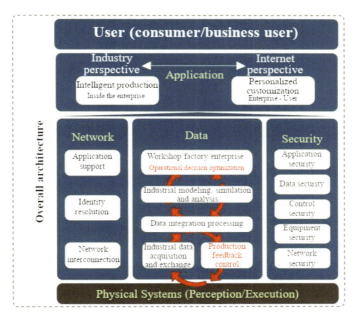

Figure 4.13 Industrial Internet architecture.

The demand for intelligent wearable products will grow rapidly in the future, but the overall manufacturing capacity cannot meet the requirements of the rapid growth and rapid changes of the industry. Consumers have put forward more complex demands for product appearance, function, and after-sales customization service. The convergence of products produced in large quantities can no longer meet the needs of consumption upgrading. High cost as well as recruitment difficulties for enterprises result in severe challenges. It is particularly urgent to upgrade the existing manufacturing mode and build a flexible, digital, and intelligent production system to adapt to the increasing personalized needs of consumers and the trend of rapid market changes.

Goertek Inc. made plans from the five aspects of the network, physical system, data, security, and application by referring to the industrial Internet architecture, as shown in Fig. 4.13.

For discrete intelligent manufacturing and large-scale personalized customization, a smart factory software/hardware collaboration solution, including head-mounted display (HMD), smartwatch, smart bracelet, and other wearable products, has been established. The scheme includes seven

78   *The World of 5G: Intelligent Manufacturing*

production lines transformation optimization (including four HMD production lines, a production line for smartwatches, and two production lines for intelligent hand rings) and two sets of system deployment (including a set of automatic storage system and a set of energy control system), two platform construction (including a set of 3D virtual plant simulation platform and a large cloud data aggregation platform), the formation of three sets of standards/drafts (including a set of draft standards for manufacturing services, a set of intelligent wearable detection standards, and a set of draft implementation specifications for the construction of smart factories).

On the one hand, the implementation of this scheme can realize the deployment and service of the same industry, and on the other hand, it can provide customized micro-services for individual consumers.

4.2.5 *Artificial takeover of intelligent assembly and industrial robots*

In the production of large enterprises, it is often involved in cross-plant and cross-region equipment maintenance, remote problem location, and other scenarios. The application of AR/VR technology in these aspects can improve the efficiency of production operation and maintenance of enterprises and reduce production costs. AR/VR brings about not only the interconnection of all things but also the information exchange of all things, allowing the maintenance work of intelligent factory to break through the boundary of the factory in the future. The factory maintenance work is completed by industrial robots or the cooperation between humans and industrial robots according to the complexity of the actual situation. In the future, every object in the factory will be a terminal with a unique IP, and the raw materials in the production process will have the property of "information". Raw materials would be automatically produced and maintained based on "information". People would have also become terminals with their own IP. People and industrial robots will enter the whole production process and conduct information interaction with raw materials, equipment, and products with unique IP. While industrial robots manage factories, human beings thousands of miles away can also receive real-time information indirectly and conduct interactive operations.

Imagine that in a smart factory covered by the 5G network in the future, when an object breaks down, the fault will be reported to the industrial robot with the highest priority and "zero" delay. Under normal circumstances, industrial robots can complete repair work without human intervention based on a database of self-learning experiences. In special cases, the industrial robot determines whether the fault must be repaired by a human.

At this time, even if people are far away from the other end of the earth, they can use a device equipped with VR and remote tactile sensing technology to remotely control the industrial robot in the factory to arrive at the fault site for repair. The industrial robot can simulate the real-time movements of people thousands of miles away, and people can carry out the construction as if they were present at the site.

AR/VR technology allows humans and industrial robots to handle more complex scenes with ease. For example, in the case of collaborative repair, even different experts from across continents can "converge" on the scene of a fault immediately, using their own VR and remote haptic sensing devices. The large flow of the 5G network can meet the mass data interaction requirements of VR high-definition images, and the extremely low time delay enables people on the other side of the earth to transmit their actions to industrial robots in the factory without error in the tactile sensing network, and multiple people can control different robots in the factory to carry out the next repair actions. At the same time, with the help of the IoT, humans and industrial robots, products, and raw materials are all directly connected to various relevant knowledge and experience databases. While conducting a fault diagnosis, humans and industrial robots can refer to a large amount of experience and professional knowledge to improve the accuracy of problem positioning.

4.2.6 *Expert business support and remote maintenance*

AR/VR is a transformative technology that can completely subvert traditional human–computer interaction content. Change is not only reflected in the consumer sector but also in many business and enterprise markets. AR/VR requires the transmission, storage, and computation of a large amount of data. If these data and computation-intensive tasks are transferred to the cloud, we can take advantage of the cloud server data storage and high speed computing power.

Maintenance mode — "Maintenance people can't come today"

That's a nightmare opening line at a time when the breakdown of production lines means the loss of money every second. But in the 5G era, "maintenance people can't come today" will be the new normal. Relax, it doesn't mean that the maintenance people can't get to the scene, but the repairman doesn't have to be there. As more equipment and components are connected to the 5G network, maintenance parties (even foreign experts across continents) can obtain fault information through the 5G network the first time after a fault occurs, "gather" at the fault site, and use VR and other technologies to guide the factory in real-time processing. More and more problems can be solved online. Besides the efficient troubleshooting, maintenance personnel do not have to travel thousands of miles.

With the rapid development of science and technology, network technology has affected all aspects of work and life, and remote technology has brought great convenience to people's daily activities. Remote office, remote training, remote conference, remote technical support, remote maintenance and management, and other application scenarios appear more and more frequently. Remote technology breaks through the limitation of time and space and can realize remote transmission and exchange of information and rational utilization of resources. This is very helpful to the development of enterprises, so it has been favored by many enterprises. The reasonable use of resources, which has been a great benefit to the development of enterprises, has also been favored by many enterprises. In April 2019, Xi'an Rongke Communication Technology Co., Ltd. (Rongke Cloud) and Tsinghua Unigroup signed a contract on the remote technical support platform. Rongke Cloud uses its own unified service platform video customer service technology to build a remote expert technical support service platform for maintenance and repair work of the China Guodian Group Corporation (Guodian), which has been recognized by Guodian. Power grid is the key to the sustainable development of energy and electricity and plays an important pivotal role in the modern energy supply system. The maintenance and repair of the State Grid is a very important link in the daily work. The remote expert technical support service platform provided by Rongke Cloud helps the maintenance personnel to troubleshoot problems in time through interactive communication between on-site technicians and remote experts, which provides convenience for the maintenance and repair work of State Grid. In the case of the increasing demand for electric energy, the State Grid needs to maintain the stable supply and operation of energy and electric power, which puts forward higher requirements for the daily maintenance of the State Grid. Through the remote expert technical support service platform, experts can provide feasible suggestions for the daily maintenance of the State Grid and help the State Grid to provide more secure and high-quality power services for people's daily life and work. At the same time, in the case of power grid failure, technical maintenance personnel can promptly repair and troubleshoot the cause of failure, which will effectively reduce the impact. However, due to the complex power grid system, the wide range involved, and many influencing factors, the on-site technical maintenance personnel have limited ability in controlling the fault maintenance. At this time, the scientific principal analysis, various case summaries, and targeted opinions provided by industry experts are of great reference value. The remote expert technical support service platform can realize the interaction, communication, and exchange between remote experts and on-site technical maintenance personnel. The AR smart glasses worn by on-site technical maintenance personnel are like a pair of invisible hands to help on-site technical maintenance personnel solve on-site problems. The remote expert technical support service platform can combine the maintenance business of Guodian, construct the maintenance experience database, form the core data knowledge base of the enterprise, and make the maintenance work of the enterprise convenient. The use of the remote expert technical support service platform can reduce the repetitive and ineffective work of maintenance personnel, help maintenance personnel find fault problems and corresponding solutions more quickly, improve the efficiency of troubleshooting problems, and promote the reliability of power supply.

The basic business idea of intelligent manufacturing is to bring high-quality products to the market more quickly through a more flexible and efficient production system. Its main advantages are as follows: (1) collaborative robots and AR smart glasses assist the staff in the entire assembly process to improve work efficiency. Collaborative robots need to constantly exchange analytical data to synchronize automated processes. AR smart glasses enable workers to complete their jobs faster and more accurately; (2) state-based monitoring, machine learning, physics-based digital simulation, and digital twinning methods are accurately used to predict the changes in future performance, so as to optimize the maintenance plan and automatically order parts, reduce downtime, and reduce maintenance costs; (3) reducing logistics and inventory costs by optimizing the accessibility and transparency of suppliers' internal and external data. Cloud-based network management solutions ensure that intelligent manufacturing shares data in a secure environment.

82 The World of 5G: Intelligent Manufacturing

Remote endoscope		
Stage	Data rate	Time delay
Stage 1: Optical endoscope	12 Mb/s	35 ms
Stage 2: 360° 4K+haptic feedback	50 Mb/s	5 ms

Remote ultrasound		
Stage	Data rate	Time delay
Stage 1: Semi-automatic, haptic feedback	15 Mb/s	10 ms
Stage 2: AI visual aid, haptic feedback	23 Mb/s	10 ms

Figure 4.14   Telemedicine.

The acceleration of population aging in Europe and Asia has been a clear trend. In the 30 years from 2000 to 2030, the share of the world's population aged over 55 will rise from 12% to 20%. Some countries, such as the UK, Japan, Germany, Italy, the US, and France, will become "super-aged", with more than 20% of their population aged over 65, according to a Moody's analysis, and better healthcare will be an important guarantee for aging societies. Over the past five years, the use of mobile Internet in medical devices has been increasing. The healthcare industry is beginning to use wearable or portable devices to integrate solutions such as remote diagnosis, remote surgery, and telemedicine monitoring, as shown in Fig. 4.14.

4.2.7 *Skilled inheritance system based on artificial intelligence teaching and virtualization training*

The rapid development of artificial intelligence will profoundly change human social life and change the world. After more than 60 years of development of the new theories and new technologies such as mobile Internet, Big Data, supercomputing, sensor network, and brain science, under the drive of strong demand of economic and social development, the development of artificial intelligence is accelerating, showing new features such as deep learning, cross-border integration, man–machine collaboration, open swarm intelligence, and autonomous control. Big

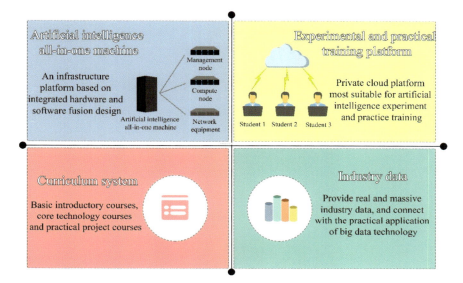

Figure 4.15 Applications of artificial intelligence.

Data-driven knowledge learning, cross-media cooperation processing, man–machine synergy to enhance intelligence, swarm integrated intelligence, and autonomous intelligent system have become the focus in the development of artificial intelligence. Brain-like intelligence inspired by brain science research is ready to take off. The trend of chip, hardware, and platform is more obvious, and the development of artificial intelligence has entered a new stage. At present, the overall advancement of the new generation of AI-related disciplines, such as theoretical modeling, technological innovation, software and hardware upgrading, is triggering a chain of breakthroughs and accelerating the leap from digitalization and networking to intelligence in all economic and social fields.

The applications of artificial intelligence are shown in Fig. 4.15.

The AI teaching platform has the following advantages.

4.2.7.1 *Plan advantages*

The design of artificial intelligence teaching and training platform for intelligent education based on cloud model comprehensively practices the concept of integration of "production, learning, application, supervision, and evaluation" and trains professional and characteristic talents from various aspects such as teaching, practice, use, monitoring, and evaluation. Students can master the basic knowledge of artificial intelligence skillfully through the teaching platform and use the knowledge they have mastered to practice in the artificial intelligence course.

The system platform scheme integrates C language, Python, and other basic programming courses. The field of artificial intelligence involves deep learning, machine learning, image recognition, natural language processing, biometric recognition, and many other aspects. The course types include basic practical training, key technology mastery, application innovation, and other practical teaching at all levels. In order to meet the needs of the artificial intelligence industry and promote the career development of students, the artificial intelligence training system based on the cloud model is planned and constructed. This system involves really cooperating with each other in the industry, school, and actual projects, giving full play to their advantages, and forming a systematic operation mode of "production, learning, application, supervision, and evaluation", so as to build the specialty with artificial intelligence characteristics.

Virtual teaching resources are used to build a practical training platform to integrate theoretical learning, practical teaching and construction, mining, storage, analysis, and actual application of artificial intelligence. From the easy to the difficult, step by step, it gradually improves students' learning skills and practical level as well as improves the quality and effectiveness of "learning". Specialized skills assessment and teaching monitoring functions are customized to form a report template for students' learning situations, major preferences, and applicable positions. It should adhere to the principle of "precision, advanced, innovative", real-time monitoring of students' operation, analysis of students' learning, and evaluating students' knowledge level, so as to reduce the pressure on the school and teachers. Teachers can carry out precise teaching according to the monitored reality, eliminating unnecessary explanation and saving a lot of time. They can analyze the evaluation report, grasp the students' learning trends, and guide the teaching accurately. The push function matches the demand template of the artificial intelligence company with the evaluation report. If the matching degree is highly consistent, it will be pushed directly to reduce the employment burden of the school and students.

4.2.7.2 *Technical advantages*

The platform adopts the private cloud mode, and all courses are conducted in the cloud. The cloud platform, independently developed and designed, can distribute hardware resources centrally. The development and operation environment required by the students' experiments are provided in a virtualized way. The experimental platform can assign an independent experimental environment for all students, provide a simple and usable development environment and can effectively manage the student resources in the environment.

Virtual reality can both provide a transferable experience and enrich our everyday non-virtual reality experiences. Through the simulation of the real world, learners are provided with the opportunity to try a variety of things. This avoids the dangers that exist in the real world and the waste of time, space, and money required in the real world.

(1) *Use virtual reality technology for knowledge learning*: Virtual reality technology, on the one hand, can easily reproduce the natural phenomena or the evolution process of things that are difficult to observe in the real world, make the abstract concept intuitive and visual and help students to understand abstract concepts and abstract things. On the other hand, virtual reality technology can enable students to conduct real-time interactive learning according to their own needs and progress and transform passive acceptance learning into active discovery learning, which can fully mobilize students' interest in learning.

(2) *Using virtual reality technology for networked teaching*: Some scenes do not exist in real life all the time, as there are time and space restrictions. Virtual reality technology can not only provide students with a situation and experience that can be found in real life but also reproduce a specific environment. With the increasing maturity of network technology and virtual reality technology, web-based virtual teaching will become a brand-new teaching method (Fig. 4.16). By combining the two, resources can be shared and transmitted in real time, so that knowledge can remain fluid and shared, and learners can learn the latest ideas immediately. The application of virtual reality technology in teaching is a beneficial supplement to the traditional education and also a reform to the traditional education. The combination of the two not only makes learners feel the joy of learning but also can provide

86 *The World of 5G: Intelligent Manufacturing*

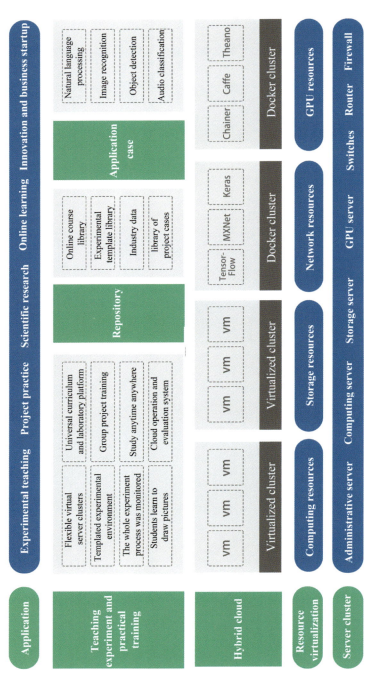

Figure 4.16 Virtualization training.

educators with rich teaching resources and produce a new teaching system.

(3) *Using virtual reality technology to conduct virtual experiments*: In experimental teaching, virtual reality technology can be used to simulate the experiments that need to be carried out with a large amount of money or some experiments with risk, severe reaction, and long time. In the virtual "lab", students can do some experiments according to their own ideas that are not suitable for doing in the real world. In the virtual experiment, students' various senses can be fully mobilized and interact with the environment, which greatly improves their interest in learning and can obtain very good learning results. In some areas, the conditions of experimental facilities are poor, and students lack the opportunity to use some instruments and reagents for experiments. In this case, virtual reality software can be used to make up for it. Students' learning is no longer restricted by learning conditions, experimental equipment, and site facilities, thus improving the quality and efficiency of learning.

4.3 Industry Robot Backed by 5G Cloud

The rapid development of 5G technology is closely linked with the growing demand for smart manufacturing for mobile Internet. With the development of the manufacturing industry to the intelligent direction, more and more new intelligent production and manufacturing equipment join the intelligent factory and gradually replace the traditional mechanical production and manufacturing equipment, such as lathe, milling machine, planer, and grinder. They constitute the intelligent production and manufacturing system. With the help of the intelligent manufacturing system, the factory not only has a more accurate digital production and processing technology but also improves the efficiency of manufacturing products. More importantly, the plant can be equipped with the ability to respond quickly to the latest market and user needs. To a certain extent, the factory can reuse the existing intelligent production and manufacturing equipment in the factory through the intelligent production and manufacturing system, so as to realize the diversification of production and meet the changing market and user needs. All of these are based on the new intelligent production and manufacturing equipment — Industrial robots.

According to the provisions of ISO (International Organization for Standardization) 8373, industrial robot is a kind of industrial automation equipment which can be fixed or moved in position and can achieve automatic control, repeatable programming, multi-function, and multi-use, with the position of the end operator being programmable within three or more degrees of freedom. According to the mechanical principles, the degree of freedom refers to the number of independent motion parameters that must be given when the mechanism has a specific motion, including translational and rotational movements of three dimensions centered on a certain axis. Taking the most typical example of industrial robots, the ubiquitous robotic arm in intelligent factories is mainly composed of a series of mutually coordinated parts. Through repeatable programming and automatic control, it participates in a specific link in the manufacturing process, such as processing, grasping, and moving a specific object.

The research and development of industrial robots involve the cooperation of several basic disciplines. For example, the research on the physical structure of industrial robots needs the support of mechanical engineering, materials science, and other fields. The research on the electronic and electrical architecture of industrial robots needs the help of electronic and electrical engineering, automation, and other fields. The research on environmental perception, decision planning, motion control, and communication algorithm of industrial robots requires cooperation from computer science, communication, artificial intelligence, deep learning, and cloud computing. The human–computer interaction mode of industrial robots also needs the support of human factors engineering and design. The intelligent integration of cross-disciplines promotes the development of industrial robots and also lays a solid foundation for the development of intelligent manufacturing driven by industrial robots.

If the specific service scope of industrial robots is mentioned, the most typical scenario is the application of industrial robots in the automobile manufacturing industry. Flexible mechanical arms in different production lines undertake different tasks in the process of vehicle production and manufacturing. For example, some are responsible for punching holes in the body of the car, some are responsible for welding the body of the car, some are responsible for carrying the door to the side of the car for auxiliary installation, and some are responsible for painting the exterior surface of the entire vehicle. They take the place of human beings in dangerous, toxic, high temperatures, and other harsh environments to repeat simple and heavy work.

Nowadays, in order to occupy a place in the fierce market competition, intelligent factories have higher and higher expectations for industrial robots. As mentioned above, smart factories need to adapt to the changing market and user needs and need to support rapid adaptive response, so as to carry out the production and manufacturing of a variety of products and ensure that smart factories are always competitive in the market. These are exactly the core requirements of the flexible production mode. In the flexible production mode, all the industrial robots in the intelligent factory should be able to organize, coordinate, and synchronize themselves to meet the needs of flexible production. But how do we realize the self-organization and coordinated synchronization between industrial robots in the factory?

First, industrial robots themselves need to be able to handle more work. This is because people expect industrial robots to be as intelligent as human beings. In the face of different external environments, they are expected to make corresponding responses with their hands, feet, and other tools based on their thinking and judgment of their "brains". With the development of artificial intelligence, deep learning, and intelligent chips, the environmental awareness and executive ability of industrial robots themselves are also gradually strengthened. All this will also bring about the possibility of the next generation of upgrading of traditional industrial robots, which can be controlled by a single program and perform simple and repetitive tasks on auxiliary manufacturing lines. Industrial robots will also become more and more intelligent under these prerequisites and then can undertake more production and manufacturing tasks alone.

Second, just as humans are socially capable, so are the expectations of industrial robots. In addition to improving its own capabilities and letting industrial robots serve a wider range, people also hope that industrial robots can have the ability to interact with the external information, transmit information, and promptly respond to the real-time demand from the remote control terminal and can cooperate with other manufacturers in the intelligent factory. The Internet plays an indispensable role in all these.

The development of Internet provides the possibility for industrial robots and external communication, but at the same time, it also brings a new problem for industrial robots and external communication — how to find a way of information transmission, which can guarantee the transmission of large amounts of data with low time delay and can guarantee the working range of industrial robots is not limited. The physical wire harness transmission can ensure the low time delay when the industrial robot communicates with the outside world, but the limitation of the working range brought by it will also affect the service coverage that the industrial robot can provide. Based on Wi-Fi and other wireless transmission methods, due to the limitation of its transmission speed, it cannot guarantee the real-time response of industrial robots when a large amount of data transmission is needed.

The arrival of the 5G era provides a solution to the above problems. People can try to build an intelligent way for communication for industrial robot and the outside world through 5G technology. This not only ensures that the industrial robot has the ability to transmit a large amount of data in real time with the outside but also can solve the problems such as the limited working range and limited-service coverage caused by the physical wire harness transmission of the industrial robot. Under such conditions, industrial robots will be upgraded from standalone intelligent devices to social intelligent devices, thus providing the possibility of their initial self-organization and coordinated synchronization.

Finally, the support of cloud computing platform is needed. If there is a computer which can be used, humans can handle more complex tasks faster. The cloud computing platform is a super-large computer in the cloud. It can provide data processing, data storage, and other services corresponding to its demand resources according to the request of any industrial robot at any time in the intelligent factory, so as to help the industrial robot deal with more complex problems faster. Because of the emergence of the cloud computing platform, all the industrial robots in the intelligent factory can be connected to the control center of the cloud with ultra-high computing power through the network, so that the "cloud brain" can manage and control all the industrial robots in the intelligent factory. This not only reduces the hardware cost and power consumption of a single industrial robot but also ensures more efficient and intelligent management. For example, the cloud platform can provide strong data support for the optimization of production and manufacturing control by collecting real-time data from industrial robots and intelligent factory assembly lines. In addition, when an industrial robot has operational failure or other problems, the cloud platform can promptly find and report them and quickly start alternative solutions.

To sum up, it is not difficult to find that the demand of intelligent factory for self-organization, coordination and synchronization, and flexible production mode among industrial robots in the factory has been transformed into the demand for 5G cloud industrial robots. With the characteristics of 5G like high speed, low time delay, and extensive connection, coupled with the cloud computing platform with infinite possibilities, multiple flexible robots in the intelligent factory can cooperate and accurately synchronize the robot formation with low time delay. This makes it possible to realize the optimization, mining, and sharing of production skills based on the Big Data cloud platform. In the following section, the role of the 5G cloud industrial robot is introduced specifically for these three parts.

4.3.1 *Cooperation of multiple flexible robots*

In factories, industrial flexible robots refer to industrial robots with more than six axes that can use the machine environment perception and positioning system and have certain image processing algorithms. Compared with the six-axis robot in the factory, the extra axis of the industrial flexible robot allows it to avoid collision through the result of environmental awareness and move to a specific position through the actuators at the end, so that it can more flexibly adapt to different working environments.

The needs of flexible manufacturing need to be adjusted by industrial flexible robots correspondingly according to the needs of different production and processing of products. The part that needs to be adjusted not only refers to the adjustment of processing technology and processing procedure but also refers to ensuring that the performance parameters of processed and to-be-processed products can also change with the change of processing methods and steps and be in line with the requirements of the corresponding production and manufacturing, so as to support rapid mass production after changes. In addition, the whole flexible manufacturing processing line also needs to have the capability of modularization and capacity expansion, and in the case of a problem of an industrial flexible robot in the processing line, the fault can be handled quickly without affecting the production capacity of the processing line.

Through the cooperation of industrial flexible robots in the production line, the automation degree in the intelligent factory can be improved at the same time, the product production efficiency can be improved, and the fault tolerance rate of the whole production line can be improved. The industrial flexible robot can deal with more processing scenes, so that the flexible manufacturing production line can be arranged more centrally, and the industrial flexible robot itself will greatly increase the frequency of use, which will also reduce the product production time. Because of the

Figure 4.17 Cooperation of multiple industrial flexible robots in automobile manufacturing.

cooperation of multiple flexible industrial robots on the production line, if one of them fails, other flexible industrial robots are also able to help it deal with the abnormal situation.

As shown in Fig. 4.17, a flexible production line composed of multiple industrial flexible robots can support the adjustment of production tasks of diversified products according to the changes in the actual demands of the market and users. However, in the deployment of traditional production line, although the connection and design between each module are relatively perfect, there are still some constraints in the actual production process due to the network deployment restrictions in the physical space. The development of 5G technology offers a solution to this physical limitation.

On the one hand, the flexible production line in the intelligent factory has high requirements for flexibility, mobility, redeployment ability, and the ability to complete various kinds of service business of the industrial flexible robot. The 5G cloud industry flexible robot has its own unique characteristics, which is conducive to the large-scale popularization of flexible production mode in intelligent factories. The arrival of the 5G cloud industry flexible robot solves this problem so that the activity area of the industrial robot is bound by the wire harness. At the same time, through the wireless connection with the cloud computing platform and unified management by the cloud computing platform, the management party can quickly adjust, update and expand the functions of multiple 5G cloud industry flexible machines which are closely coordinated in the production line when required and can move, combine and split them freely, thus complete the corresponding task requirements in different production lines more smoothly.

On the other hand, in the face of different production tasks, flexible industrial robots in the flexible production line have different demands on the network while they're in charge of different processing tasks and at different times. For example, when producing a product, there will be some processing procedures with high requirements for accuracy, which are closely related to the time delay. For example, some key processing tasks will require the close cooperation of multiple 5G cloud industry flexible robots. When faced with different production tasks, the 5G cloud industry flexible robot on the flexible production line will be adjusted to some degree, so its corresponding network and communication relations will also change accordingly. All this will be achieved based on the development of 5G technology. 5G technology with SDN (software-defined network), NFV (network function virtualization), and the network's ability to slice can support the production line according to different production and processing content of each component to carry on the flexible network architecture arrangement and can provide the exclusive transmission network on demand, adjust the allocation of network resources on demand and provide the appropriate network control function and performance guarantee for different production links by means of bandwidth restriction and priority configuration.

In the cooperation of many industrial flexible robots, 5G cloud industrial flexible robots interact with cloud computing platforms for a large number of real-time data through cloud. After collecting these data, the cloud computing platform will conduct unified management of the 5G cloud industry flexible robots on the production line, strengthen the coordination between the 5G cloud chemical industry flexible robots and complete the tasks that a single flexible industrial robot cannot complete independently.

The cooperation of multiple industrial flexible robots not only refers to the cooperation among them but also the cooperation between one or more flexible robots and human beings should be considered. With the low delay characteristic of 5G, flexible industrial robots can respond quickly and give feedback after sensing workers' movements, cooperate with workers, and help workers complete production and manufacturing tasks faster.

4.3.2 *Industrial control robot formation with low time delay and precision synchronization*

With the deepening of the research on multi-robot cooperation, the formation thinking of multi-robot comes into being. Multi-robot formation is a kind of control technology in which multiple robots can keep a certain assembled formation and avoid obstacles in the process of moving to the destination. Multi-robot formation is a typical multi-robot cooperative system. The study of multi-robot formation plays an important role in promoting the optimization of multi-robot cooperative control.

When it comes to industrial robot fleets, automated guided vehicles (AGVs) in intelligent factories come to mind. Using environment-aware sensors, each vehicle can automatically drive from its starting point to its destination on a pre-set moving path without the need for external guidance. In the course of driving, if the environment sensing sensor of the vehicle detects obstacles in front of the driving path, the vehicle will also take corresponding obstacle avoidance strategies, such as stopping and waiting. With the help of unmanned transport vehicles, intelligent factories can realize functions such as automatic loading, unloading, and handling of goods within the factory.

The AGVs in the intelligent plant move according to the pre-set route and solve the problem of transportation of factory goods. This seems to be a good solution. However, with the expansion of the scale of the factory, the existing AGVs cannot undertake all the cargo loading and unloading and handling work in the factory, so the number of AGVs in the factory would also be increased. But how can we let so many AGVs in the factory efficiently complete the work of cargo handling? We need to consider from the perspective of how to coordinate the resources of the whole plant. The most simple and effective idea is to put a large number of AGVs into formation.

The most common formation control is based on leader–follower formation control. The basic idea is that all the AGVs in the formation will be divided into two roles: leader and follower. The leader will drive automatically according to the pre-set route and control the movement trend of the whole team, while the followers will follow the leader through the relative position between the leader and them. The formation control method based on leader–follower is simple and easy to implement. However, this formation is more dependent on the leader. If the leader part fails or the information is incorrect, the operation of the whole team will be stopped.

One may wonder if, in formation, the path itself could be used as a benchmark instead of a special leader and follower. The formation control method based on the path following is thus developed. The basic idea is to decompose the task of formation control in time and space and get the coordinated synchronous task in time and the path following task in space, so as to realize the coordinated synchronous formation control. When using this method, you need to specify a leader as a reference point. The formation control method based on path following has a relatively small amount of data to interact with each robot, which can be used in the environment with limited communication. So if the robot itself enters the area of unstable signal transmission in a short time, the robot can still follow the pre-set path.

The above two methods of formation have their own advantages, but in an intelligent factory, the position and speed of multiple industrial robots and the situation of dangerous obstacles around each industrial robot can be obtained not only based on its own sensors and algorithms but also through information interaction between various industrial robots or between industrial robots and the cloud. Then can multiple industrial robots try to control the formation through the real-time transmission of these intelligent information? Advances in artificial intelligence, deep learning, cloud computing, Big Data, and 5G technology make this possible. Through the formation of multiple robots, the real-time status of each member in the team and in other teams is collected, and then useful information is quickly arranged and transmitted to each member in the cloud management system, so as to realize the idea of real-time formation control based on intelligent information transmission.

Of course, there are many methods for formation control of multiple robots, such as formation control method based on artificial potential field and formation control method based on behavior. According to the specific scene and the specific manufacturing needs, the appropriate formation method can be selected to promote the cooperation between various industrial robots in factories. When considering which formation mode is more suitable for the current situation of the factory, it can also be analyzed from the following points:

(1) *The length of the path*: The ratio of the average distance traveled by multiple robots from the starting point to the target point to the straight-line distance between the starting point and the target point. The smaller the value, the more effective the corresponding formation method is.

96   *The World of 5G: Intelligent Manufacturing*

(2) *Formation maintenance*: The ratio of the robot in the desired position at different moments of movement. The smaller the value, the better the formation can be maintained in the presence of obstacles.
(3) *Allowed time*: The time required for multiple robots to reach their destination and form a formation.
(4) *The cost of obstacle avoidance*: The number of times that multiple robots collide with obstacles during operation. The fewer collisions, the better the obstacle avoidance algorithm.

Multiple robots' formation can be used to improve the efficiency of the robot to accomplish complex tasks, and different ways of formation can also improve the adaptability, robustness, and flexibility of multiple robots in the face of unknown scenes and strengthen the cooperation between multiple robots, so that industrial robots can finish the tasks assigned by factories faster. The development of artificial intelligence, deep learning, Big Data, cloud computing technology, etc., provides the foundation for realizing all these, and the development of 5G technology opens the channel between them, making it possible for the large-scale promotion in the factories.

4.3.3 *The optimization, mining and sharing mode of production skills based on Big Data cloud platform*

As described in Chapter 3, 5G has three typical application scenarios: eMBB, Massive Machine Type Communication (mMTC), and ultra-reliable Low-latency Communication (uRLLC). eMBB is mainly oriented to large-flow mobile broadband services, such as 3D/ultra-high-definition video resource transmission and video live broadcast, which is embodied in the ultra-high data transmission rate. With 5G, we can play AR/VR games online as easily as the main character in the movie Ready Player One, and the peak speed can reach 10 Gb/s. mMTC is mainly oriented to large-scale IoT business and relies on the powerful connection capacity of 5G to realize the interconnection of everything, from small smart homes to large smart factories and smart cities, all of which will be within reach in daily life and industrial production with the support of 5G. In the smart factory, a large number of industrial robots sense the surrounding environment and identify the working target through sensors to ensure smooth production and send the sensor data to the cloud platform through the back-end network. The cloud platform sends instructions based on the data and sends them back to the robot itself. If these processes are transmitted through the existing network, there will be obvious delay, which makes it easy to cause production safety accidents. However, the low delay of 5G can ensure safe and orderly production.

On the one hand, the development of the 5G network will promote the development of artificial intelligence technology to a certain extent, thus promoting the development of industrial robots themselves, improving production efficiency and quality, and promoting the development of the entire industry. On the other hand, 5G technology can greatly improve the data acquisition and transmission speed. Industrial robots can connect to the cloud Big Data cloud platform through 5G network and carry out real-time control, monitoring, and maintenance of the manufacturing process through Big Data and artificial intelligence technology.

So, how do industrial robots and cloud platforms work together? We can simply think of cloud platforms as remote computers that can store and process huge amounts of data. If your PC isn't configured to support your favorite big game, your PC can lag while you play, seriously affecting your gaming experience and performance. At this point, if you connect to the cloud platform with strong computing capacity through the 5G network, you can use the remote computer of the cloud platform to process the resources consumed by the game and solve the problem of game lag without improving the configuration of your PC. It can be seen that the hardware cost and power consumption of the robot itself can be greatly reduced by moving the data storage and computing capacity required by the industrial robot to the cloud platform based on Big Data. In the whole life cycle of a product, from planning and design to procurement and production, from circulation and sales to after-sales service, then to the final product recovery and disposal, each link will produce a huge amount of data. We will collect these data and send them to the cloud platform for autonomous learning through artificial intelligence technology, which enables the cloud platform to have the ability of emergency judgment and provide excellent solutions to various situations in various production processes to deal with various production problems.

In a smart factory, the 5G network will cover every corner and connect intelligent industrial robots together through its strong interconnection ability to ensure that they can communicate with each other. The production and manufacturing involved include processing, transportation, warehousing, and other links of the program decision, making the production more intelligent, customized, and efficient. Massive data is the basis of artificial intelligence, and a variety of sensors on industrial robots are the main way to obtain data on cloud platforms. In addition to the status information of the equipment itself, the cloud platform based on Big Data can also collect information about the production environment, the quality of raw materials and auxiliary materials, the specific conditions of the processing process, and other information inside the factory. These can also be transmitted as valid data to the cloud platform for computing. These data can be used for product process optimization, equipment failure prediction, product quality inspection, inventory management, and so on.

But how does that work? After the cloud platform collects a large amount of data from industrial robots in factories, we can build a cloud platform data center based on these large amounts of data and conduct rapid and professional mining and processing of the data in the cloud platform data center. For example, the real-time production situation of a factory can be simulated through the real-time data of a factory to assist in monitoring the production and manufacturing situation in the factory, or the failure of an industrial robot in a factory can be found in time and the corresponding solution can be provided. When the analysis results or quantifiable solutions based on real-time data are obtained, the cloud platform data center needs to transmit the analysis conclusions back to the intelligent factory as soon as possible. After the intelligent factory receives these information, it can rationalize the layout of the factory according to its suggestions, so as to strengthen the collaborative work of all industrial robots in the factory and improve the production and manufacturing efficiency. Among them, real-time data transmission brought about by 5G communication technology is essential.

4.4 Customized Production of the Whole Life Cycle of Products Supported by 5G

Since the reform and opening up, China has experienced a period of accelerated development of urbanization and industrialization, and residents' consumption patterns have undergone fundamental changes. The rise of the Internet has led to a new round of consumption upgrading. In this era of the Internet of everything, the establishment of a consumer-oriented thinking model is increasingly important for the development of a business. This even can be counted as a key link for the survival of a business. In this way of thinking, the ideal market system is to provide each consumer with the perfect idea to solve their pain points at the most appropriate time. Today's market system, however, is still far from achieving this ultimate goal. Based on the characteristics and key technologies of 5G described above, the customized production of enterprises can better meet the needs of consumers and further get close to the ultimate goal of the market system. At present, the gradual decline of the return on investment has made the investment-driven growth model difficult to sustain, and the change of the international environment has led to the weak export. How to further promote the upgrading of residents' consumption and release the consumption potential has become a top priority.

4.4.1 *Online customer customization system based on 5G AR-Cloud*

Each individual consumer has his/her own preference, product focus, and unique aesthetic, so business managers should shift their attention from media, channels, and audience groups to personalized personal information. An important part of the success of Haidilao (Sichuan Haidilao Catering Co., Ltd.) lies in its ability to provide personalized services for different customers. For example, it provides female customers with manicure services, while providing shoe polishing service for male clients; when customers wear glasses for dinner, the waiter will provide a disposable alcohol non-woven cloth to wipe the glasses in time; when there are children dining, they will give children gift bags and so on. With the orientation of consumers and the provision of personalized services, Haidilao stands out from many hotpot catering enterprises. It ranked first among the TOP20 Chinese hotpot restaurants in terms of turnover in 2019.

So, let's get back to the manufacturing industry, compared with many enterprises for mass production of traditional fuel cars, new energy vehicle enterprises consider more thoughtfully the personalized customization of production for consumers. GAC New Energy (i.e., Guangzhou Automobile Group Co., Ltd.) is such a digital intelligent factory in which highly personalized customization can be realized. Through the user-exclusive app launched by GAC New Energy (Fig. 4.18), consumers can not only customize the color of the car body, the color of the interior, and the fabric of the seat but also choose the technological configuration. In the future, consumers will even be able to customize the battery capacity.

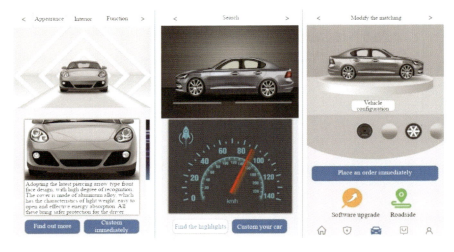

Figure 4.18   Customization mobile phone app for GAC new energy vehicles.

As the world's leading interactive customization factory, the factory of GAC New Energy enables users to realize personalized customization of vehicles through their mobile apps. Its unique customized production mode of "user experience of the whole process" enables mass customization and ensures product quality. What is worth mentioning is that users who order a car can also watch a live broadcast of the key manufacturing process of their car online through their own apps and watch the moment when the car is off the production line. The smart factory of GAC New Energy makes use of advanced technology to make the "transparent factory" and "transparent workshop" become a reality. From customized production to quality management and then to delivery, the smart factory of GAC New Energy will permeate the digital strategy into the whole value chain, which will bring the direct effect of further improvement of efficiency and further highlighting of personalization.

In order to better serve customers and provide consumers with a more convenient and intuitive immersive product experience, the company applies the AR/VR technology mentioned above to automotive product customization service and builds 5G AR-Cloud customer online customization system. On the one hand, this system can provide customers with a more convenient purchasing experience, while on the other hand, it can also enable enterprises to better display the characteristics of the product.

The Application of Intelligent Mass Production Based on 5G 101

In the case of car manufacturers, AR/VR and online video can be widely used in online car buying services. An Internet platform for an intelligent manufacturing industry is built based on 5G features, which can provide data-based intelligent cloud services and upload customizable modeling data of body lamps, body color, body tail, interior style, interior materials, tire size, wheel spoke style, front and rear suspension, medium and low matching to the cloud. All these are now possible thanks to 5G's high speed, low-latency, and wide connectivity capabilities. Equipment, application systems, and operators' terminals of industrial enterprises can all be connected to the cloud service platform, and the data on the cloud platform can be updated by multiple parties according to unified standards, so as to realize the rapid update of multiple terminals. In the app (user side), with eMBB being one of the three scenarios of 5G, the 5G super-high-speed network can quickly synchronize the cloud data to the user terminal, support personalized car selection application, and combine with AR technology to achieve an immersive experience. Users can open the door to observe the internal configuration and model of the vehicle seat, central control platform, main display, and other operations and can also turn on the headlights, turn signals, interior atmosphere light, and other operations, fully experiencing every detail of the customized vehicle. The customization of the vehicle can be realized through real-time interaction with the factory.

In other words, customers can intuitively experience the interior and exterior styling and texture of the customized vehicle they choose before paying. At the same time, AR technology can be used to simulate vehicle driving. After reading the vehicle kinematics model in the cloud, simulation driving can be realized under different road conditions, weather conditions, and traffic conditions to show the performance of the vehicle chassis and dynamic modeling of the vehicle. As for the driving experience and power performance of the vehicle, you can go to the 4S shop (automobile sales and service 4S shop) to drive and ride the same model configuration of the physical car for a real experience.

In addition to the application of vehicle presentation, with 5G, the time and space distance between sales staff and customers can be well-crossed. Sales personnel only need to wear VR headsets or glasses, and they can synchronously introduce and explain the characteristics of the vehicle products selected by customers remotely, so that customers can experience more friendly service, and it is also convenient for the manufacturers to promote products. It is predictable that 5G will play a

102 *The World of 5G: Intelligent Manufacturing*

disruptive role in both product sales and consumer consumption. The multi-dimensional marketing model established from this will also benefit most people.

4.4.2 *Aided design of intelligent products based on Big Data + IoT*

Usually, when we use a mobile app, we often meet the following situation: after you search a certain sports goods in the shopping mall, the system will automatically push the related sports goods to you. After you use a search engine to search for a certain toiletry, web ads will also send you a purchase link for the relevant product. To better serve consumers, marketers will begin to think more broadly about their brands' points of contact with their customers. Google and Facebook have a good grasp of market dynamics, and Facebook in particular is well-positioned because the whole company is built around the concept that user profiles are a basic marketing unit. Every time you click on a website, the Internet company uploads it to a database. They use algorithms such as machine learning to deeply analyze user data and predict future consumption trends of related products. Internet companies know that whoever controls more data can gain more initiative in the marketplace. Google and Facebook, which control the largest third-party databases, want other companies to upload primary data so that Google and Facebook can aggregate it with the large number of third-party databases they already control.

With the arrival of the 5G era, the technologies of NB-IoT and mMTC will be widely used in the IoT, and the IoT will usher in great opportunities. With the Internet of everything, every trip you make and every search on the Internet and any malfunction in your car can be reperceived by car manufacturers or third-party companies. They use the corresponding artificial intelligence algorithm to train the model on different data, so that they can perceive the changing trend of users' preferences the first time and provide a reference for the development of new products. This makes it possible to make full use of Big Data + IoT to promptly get the data of users and potential users in the process of product design and to assist the design of products through the modeling, analysis, and prediction of Big Data.

In the era of Internet of everything, the biggest change in the automotive ecosystem comes from the main engine plants. For a 4S shop or dealer, this is a revolutionary change. There will be new service and marketing methods such as sales promotion of new models based on AR/VR, real-time push of customer information in stores, and real-time monitoring of customer vehicle maintenance. But it is the effective use of Big Data in the era of the Internet that embodies the greatest value of this era. Only the main engine plants can fully integrate and utilize the upstream and downstream data of the industry. The traditional user researcher may become a data specialist, and the traditional may become a data center. Product planners can obtain Big Data of customers and industries from the shared database, process it with algorithms such as machine learning, and the system will automatically analyze and evaluate it, so as to provide reasonable suggestions for the development and upgrade of new products. The product manager does not have to study those tedious vehicle parameters when they want to make the most reasonable plan for the development or upgrade of products.

With the improvement of living standards, new changes have taken place in people's requirements for travel. Nowadays, what people need is not only vehicle mobility but also the maneuverability of driving and the comfortable experience of driving and even the health index of the environment in the car cabin. Automobile manufacturing is no longer only concerned with the balance between vehicle performance and fuel economy, but has evolved into a management process of travel experience centered on the feelings of drivers and passengers. This means that the construction of the IoT, which carries customers' travel and life behaviors, plays a key role in realizing this goal.

The arrival of 5G makes the IoT ecosystem possible to achieve this goal. On a larger scale, the ecosystem could include at least billions of low powers, low bit-rate wearables, home devices, temporary wearables, and remote sensors. Based on the real-time data of customer consumption level and travel mode provided by these instruments, product managers or management personnel of main engine plants can effectively obtain and evaluate the vehicle features that all consumer groups are most concerned about. These data can also be used for predictive analysis, allowing main engine plants to quickly identify potential consumers, thus making product development more directional and greatly reducing the time and money spent on early product development.

With the development of the Internet, the driving data and other information of many models will be continuously uploaded to the manufacturer's cloud server, and the technology has also shifted to the more advanced IoT and cloud computing. For example, travel miles are collected through wheel speed mileage sensor equipment. Through the IoT, manufacturers can predict the changing trend of travel mileage of a certain consumer group and evaluate the vehicle accident rate. Based on this, they can provide data support for the design of new models or the upgrade of models. With the advent of the 5G era, the collection function of user information will become more powerful. IoT devices can constantly collect customer-specific data, quickly process, analyze and return information, and deliver customized ads to specific customers. This will enable the manufacturer to greatly reduce the cost of advertising promotion and can design products more in line with consumer needs according to dynamically updated information.

Of course, this is just the beginning. In the 5G era, the collection of user information is more convenient. In the field of product planning, timeliness and comprehensiveness of data are very important. What the 5G network can provide is more and more complete real-time transmission of user data. Devices and sensors in the ecosystem of IoT can help people plan different development plans for different consumer groups after gathering all available user information. Not only the customers of the local brand products but also the potential customers would be identified by the model run by the cloud platform in the IoT, which will be fed back to the management of product development in real time to adjust the product development plan.

4.4.3 *Small-scale customized production based on ultra-flexible manufacturing*

The online customer customization system based on 5G AR-Cloud and the intelligent product auxiliary design based on Big Data + IoT enable manufacturers to design the corresponding products according to the needs of users with a more agile response speed. From the manufacturer's perspective, when a product is developed, tested, and ready for market, it needs to be made known to the public through third parties (TV ads, online tweets, and posters) and then a distribution system must be provided. The traditional sales method of automobile manufacturers is generally the method of distribution points, including the first-tier cities and the cities where 4S stores are located.

This marketing method is still in use today, but it has an obvious drawback. Due to the lack of Big Data feedback, manufacturers don't really know how well their campaigns are working, so they keep laying out outlets to cover as many territories as possible, but the reality is that they don't always reach all the territories. Therefore, in order to evaluate the acceptability and popularity of the products in the market before mass manufacturing and to avoid quality problems or design defects of the products, we can conduct a trial production of the products in small batches and offer them to customers for a trial experience. Based on this demand, small-scale customized production of flexible manufacturing is an essential link for manufacturers.

Let's get back to the smart factory of GAC New Energy. In terms of "smart manufacturing", the smart factory has the first domestic assembly line for steel and aluminum bodies, with the highest production efficiency in the industry, which can realize the automatic flexible switch of six models within one minute. Digital simulation and virtual debugging technology are adopted in the whole production process, which reduces the on-site debugging time to 35%. Intelligent ecological positioning can be reflected in the factory's intelligent logistics, intelligent collaborative production equipment, 3D visual guidance technology, intelligent automatic assembly technology, and other aspects. It is a "smart" production line. In addition, the smart factory also adopts the linear seven-axis robot continuous production mode. Compared with the traditional mode, the stamping equipment does not need to stop and wait at the upper limit, and the motor braking and starting time can be cut by 98%, which plays a role in energy saving. Among them, production automation refers to the convergence of industry-leading automatic production technology. 100% automatic installations are realized for chassis assembly, windshield glasses and seats, fully covering independent identification, sensing, human–computer interaction, and other information equipment and making the production simpler, more efficient, and more accurate. Digitization of information refers to the comprehensive realization of "digitization" of information of workshop management elements, synchronous development of vehicle models and enterprise management, based on the advanced technology of the IoT, to build a comprehensive visual and traceable and efficient "transparent factory". Intelligent management refers to the implementation of "intelligent key process equipment", "intelligent logistics equipment", and "intelligent management auxiliary decision-making" with the industry's first "intelligent manufacturing execution system" (IMES) as the brain. Intelligent manufacturing is ecological, which means that through equipment technology upgrading, the number of water-saving and environment-friendly processes, the use of clean energy, and so on, the smoke and dust, wastewater, and waste gas emissions are greatly reduced, the factory is more energy-efficient and ecological, and the social responsibility is fulfilled.

The smart factory of GAC New Energy constantly seeks breakthroughs in process technology. Taking the industry's first "intelligent manufacturing execution system" as the brain, GAC implements "intelligent key process equipment", "intelligent logistics equipment", and "intelligent management auxiliary decision-making", fully realizes "intelligent management", and can constantly iterate and update.

The smart factory of GAC New Energy has reached the world's leading level. If it can make full use of the technology features of 5G to connect the IoT between actuators and controllers on the production line and between actuators, the factory will no longer need complex cables for data transmission, and each system can be directly controlled through transmission wirelessly. When the cables disappear, the cost of buying and maintaining them will be reduced, and the safety risks caused by the cables will be greatly reduced. In addition, the factory can realize the vision of remote synchronous operation of equipment and massive connection of equipment. Based on the Big Data platform, it can provide the whole life cycle management of equipment, realize the remote operation and maintenance of equipment, open up the data flow of the supply chain, and synergistically optimize the upstream and downstream design of the supply chain. At the same time, applications like data monitoring, high-definition camera/photography in the use of process management/factory security brought by sensing equipment, field AGV wireless cloud control, and asset management and tracking have been further strengthened. 5G technology under the application of "intelligent manufacturing" can help enterprises to reduce costs and increase efficiency. It is also an opportunity for enterprises to rethink their value positioning and restructure their business model.

As shown in Fig. 4.19, based on 5G technology, information infrastructure can be highly interconnected, industrial-level real-time systems can be built, more flexible and intelligent factories can be built, and the soaring cost can be controlled. With the disappearance of cables, the "ropes" that restrict the movement of robots disappear. With the continuous coverage of high-reliability network, robots can be put on wheels (or other devices) to move around the factory at will and reach various

The Application of Intelligent Mass Production Based on 5G 107

Figure 4.19 Flexible switching welding system for multi-vehicle models independently developed by GAC New Energy.

locations on demand, which will bring great imagination space to the production mode of the factory. At the moment when flexible manufacturing is increasingly emphasized, a flexible production line that can flexibly adjust the position of each equipment and allocate tasks will become a new "magic weapon" for producers. The ultra-high-speed transmission of 5G greatly facilitates the detection and management of information, so that the "perception" between various components will be more accurate and rapid, and the degree of intelligence can be greatly improved. The management of traditional industrial manufacturing and production has been affected by the mechanical thinking mode for a long time, which lacks flexibility and variability, leading to rigid production management. While the concept of "Industry 4.0" focuses on flexible production. Flexibility will be the core competitiveness of future industrial processing and manufacturing production. Different from the traditional screw-type production line, flexible manufacturing is committed to the flexibility, adjustability, and variability of processing and manufacturing. It aims at maximizing production efficiency and optimizing the allocation of resources, so as to minimize costs and improve profits in all links. Due to the transformation of traditional production, various countries now have an urgent need for talents in this field, especially professional management talents. As a result, many top universities are also setting up new disciplines, such as industrial engineering, to cultivate talents in this field.

Flexibility and scalability are key features of the 5G network. Rather than relying on manual management, this kind of network requires a fully automated network management technique such as self-diagnosing, self-healing, self-configuring, self-optimizing, and auto-install/plug-and-play, which is the foundation for efficient network operations and a dynamic portfolio of services. With the development of automated network management technology, the management will become more flexible and adaptable. This kind of management needs new tools. In particular, 5G networks should consider AI and automatic learning technologies, which will be more conducive to flexible manufacturing in production lines. 5G takes advantage of its unique and incomparable advantages to facilitate the large-scale popularization of flexible production.

For the vehicle manufacturing plant, the building of the 5G IoT cloud platform can be divided into three layers: the edge connection layer, the infrastructure layer, and the application service layer. Among them, the edge connection layer is mainly responsible for collecting data and transferring it to the cloud. The infrastructure layer provides a globally secure cloud infrastructure to meet the needs of daily industrial workloads and oversight. The application service layer is mainly responsible for providing the framework of industrial terminal equipment and various service interactions. It mainly provides the environment and terminal equipment for creating, testing, and running industrial Internet programs, which can realize the collaboration between equipment, system, and controller.

This enables the production line to standardize and organize all kinds of data according to unified standards through the cloud platform and provide services for retrieval and analysis at any time. With the industrial cloud platform based on 5G, the whole vehicle production line can realize the full recording of the production process, wireless intelligent positioning, and overall data presentation (capacity/yield/material loss, etc.). For example, the manufacturing process of the whole vehicle can realize real-time monitoring of equipment energy consumption. Through this platform, real-time monitoring and fault feedback service of equipment can be realized as well as visual management of equipment operation data, which can meet the high level of workshop safety standards. The platform determines the optimal safe maintenance period after analyzing the parameters by referring to the life cycle model of equipment and provides real-time early warning service for the equipment with a high-risk coefficient.

4.5 5G Facilitates Intelligent Resource Allocation

"4G changes life, 5G changes society". As the development direction of a new round of mobile communication technology, 5G extends the connection from people to the Internet of everything and also brings better wireless solutions to key links of intelligent manufacturing such as warehouse management and logistics supply, which improves the intelligent level of the industry.

4.5.1 *5G helps intelligent warehouse management*

A stereoscopic warehouse is controlled and managed by a computer, which has the characteristics of high utilization rate of space and strong ability of output and input. It is helpful for enterprises to implement modern management, so it is paid more and more attention by enterprises. With the rapid development of science and technology, information technology, and automated production technology, the handling, storage, distribution, and corresponding information of raw materials, semi-finished products, finished products, and various materials in the circulation link in the production process are not isolated events. The traditional intelligent three-dimensional warehouse includes warehouse control system (WCS) and warehouse management system (WMS), and the warehouse information needs to be transmitted back to the computer control management software for analysis and processing. However, due to the slow transmission rate of the 4G network and high time delay, inventory cannot be promptly taken in traditional warehouse management and they cannot be automatically replenished either.

Based on mass network, instant communication, low delay, high reliability, and other technologies, intelligent warehouse management can track the material information in real time and realize continuous replenishment. The relationship between different parts is coordinated in a guiding way to promote the efficient flow of the stereoscopic warehouse and meet the demand of the new flexible manufacturing. The functional features and advantages of 5G lie in reducing the time delay of the traditional intelligent stereoscopic warehouse, improving the computing capacity of the intelligent stereoscopic warehouse and realizing the self-operation of the storage system. When the intelligent stereoscopic warehouse monitors the storage location information, it analyzes the operation of the materials in the production line at the edge and uses the characteristics of

110 *The World of 5G: Intelligent Manufacturing*

5G to speed up the storage to obtain the demand and inventory information of the production line. At the same time, the intelligent stereoscopic warehouse sends the order of picking up and replenishing goods to the transport devices. In this way, the information exchange from the end of the stereoscopic warehouse to the end of the production line and the end of the transportation equipment is realized, the overall storage system is optimized, and the production efficiency and modern management level of the enterprise are improved.

4.5.2 5G will boost intelligent logistics supply

4.5.2.1 *Intelligent logistics supply based on 5G*

In recent years, under the dual impetus of economic globalization and e-commerce, traditional logistics has been rapidly transforming to modern logistics, thus becoming the development trend in the future. Intelligent logistics has become the key factor to promote the transformation and upgrading of modern logistics. At present, logistics enterprises' demand for intelligent logistics mainly includes three fields: logistics data, logistics cloud, and logistics equipment. With the promotion and application of 5G technology, the domestic logistics industry will usher in new development opportunities. The intelligent logistics market has a broad prospect. As an inseparable and important part of the 5G industry chain, logistics will undergo great changes due to the generation of 5G. Therefore, the value of 5G for logistics is self-evident. According to the current exploration of many enterprises, we can see that 5G will transform the traditional logistics industry from several aspects.

With the application of RFID, EDI, and other technologies, the development of intelligent logistics supply has almost solved all kinds of problems of traditional logistics warehousing. But at present, AGV scheduling usually adopts the Wi-Fi communication mode, which is vulnerable to interference, switching, and insufficient coverage ability. It is hard for the 4G network to support the information construction of intelligent logistics. How to efficiently and quickly use the database to coordinate each link of the logistics supply chain, so that the whole logistics supply chain system is economical and operated efficiently, is a difficult problem faced by the manufacturing industry. The high speed of 5G is conducive to parameter estimation and can provide support for high precision ranging and accurate positioning. The characteristics of the 5G network with low delay can make each link of logistics more quickly, intuitively and accurately obtain relevant data. The data of logistics transportation and goods loading and picking up can reach the user end, the management end, and the operation end more quickly. The feature of the 5G wide connection also enables more AGVs to work together in the same section at the same time point.

Intelligent logistics based on 5G focuses on self-decision-making of equipment, self-management of resources and self-planning of paths, so as to realize the allocation of resources on demand. Establishing device-to-device (D2D) real-time communication through the 5G network transmission technology with the characteristic of low latency and using the slice in 5G network technology to improve high aging and low energy consumption of resource allocation finally helped realize the intelligence of AGV in intelligent factory scheduling and multi-machine cooperation, making the production process and material flow information reach the equipment end, production end, and management end faster and result in end-to-end seamless docking.

A set of intelligent tooling distribution system includes AGV equipment (integrated forklift function), code scanning and work card identification equipment, handheld terminal calling equipment, scheduling system, equipment for information interaction with the tooling management system, automatic charging pile, etc. The tooling information about the dispatching system is sent through a handheld terminal calling device. The dispatching system obtains the worker's station information, worker's identity information and material information through the instruction issued by the worker and then assigns the appropriate AGV to the material area. The AGV needs to be equipped with an RFID identifier to automatically identify and transfer materials according to the instructions given by the dispatching system. The materials shall be transferred from the storage area or the stereoscopic garage to the workstation, and the AGV independently plans the optimal path to reach the destination. The 5G transmitted images are used for real-time obstacle avoidance through the deep learning platform, and the elevator door of the workshop is also required to be automatically opened and closed. After arriving at the workstation, the workers can complete the material registration through the employee card or other scanning equipment before extracting. After completion, the AGV will continue to distribute or rest in the designated area (automatic charging) according to the instructions of the dispatching system without personnel interference in the distribution. This is the intelligent logistics supply based on 5G.

4.5.2.2 *Full supply chain management based on 5G information flow*

At present, the manufacturing industry is facing the pressure of transformation from cost advantage to technology advantage and constantly develops new products with high technology content and independent intellectual property rights, which has become the focus of competition in the manufacturing industry chain. Traditional product development usually adopts the engineering method of sequential operation. The design, process, inspection, and manufacturing of an enterprise are all independent activities, so are the organization and management. Designers are often unable to consider the manufacturing process problems, resulting in a disjoint in the design and manufacturing process, and at the same time, product quality cannot be guaranteed. With high speed, low delay, and wide connection network, the 5G communication system can realize multi-channel high-definition video return and real-time data analysis feedback. At the same time, the security and stability of 5G are further optimized on the basis of the original 4G network, which can meet most customers' demands who have higher requirements for factory information security. VR technology will assist in industrial design, allowing multiple remote workers to enter the same virtual scene to co-design products.

Modern supply chain is a complex network chain structure composed of suppliers, manufacturers, distributors and customers, and the input points that support the overall chain structure come only from the payment customers make when they buy the products produced by the supply chain operation. Thus, how to manage the supply chain and reduce the operation cost in the supply chain is the research focus of the supply chain. The research results show that in the operation process of the supply chain, the nodes at all levels are expanding the supply and demand information to avoid risks, so that more and more fluctuations appear in the demand information. Using Big Data to integrate the existing data in the supply chain can effectively reduce the large amount of high inventory in the supply chain.

The most important point in the model is to ensure data connectivity and delivery efficiency. The organizational structure of the model can guarantee the timeliness and consistency of data in the structure. Ensuring the timeliness and consistency of information acquisition is the key consideration of this model. The main application scenarios, business needs, and challenges faced by the mobile Internet and the real network shall also be considered. High expectations are placed on the timeliness and fluidity of information collection. Therefore, in the development process of the supply chain, it is an urgent task to realize logistics dynamic information collection and commodity information network sharing. Current information-gathering technologies enhance connectivity and mobility to a certain extent, but there is still a long way to go to meet the growing needs of personalization. The development of 5G mobile communication technology and the advancement of formal commercialization provide technical support to solve this problem.

The cooperative inventory management information acquisition system of supply chain based on 5G technology has the following functions:

(1) *Automatic identification*: For example, the data of circulation, transfer and processing of products in the supply chain can be automatically identified by RFID and automatic identification technologies.
(2) *Automatic storage and transmission*: The information is stored in the device and automatically transferred to the collaborative inventory management database of the supply chain.
(3) *On-site operation*: The storage and recovery of terminal data are read and controlled remotely to realize on-site reading and setting of parameters through mobile terminal devices.
(4) *Protection of data*: To prevent data loss caused by abnormal data or unexpected events, real-time data backup can be achieved.
(5) *Correct judgment*: The intelligent supply chain created by 5G cloud intelligence and supply chain collaborative management system can judge the wrong or deviated data of the terminal, display the error, classify and process the data deviating from the normal system, and intelligently judge whether it belongs to valid data or abnormal analysis.
(6) *Measurement of parameters*: Input parameters are set according to field conditions or actual needs to achieve different monitoring and control.
(7) *Self-examination*: It includes the functions of self-check of remote control terminal and communication detection.

The system can be divided into four layers: data collection layer, network transmission layer, data storage layer, and data application layer.

4.5.2.3 *Application scenarios of modern logistics based on the 5G network*

According to the *Application of 5G Network Technology in the New Generation Logistics Industry* released by YTO Research Institute, the application of 5G in various logistics scenarios will be realized in four stages.

Stage 1: Based on the high speed characteristics of 5G, the main service scenario is eMBB, and the specific applications include logistics application of augmented reality, logistics data computing platform, and blockchain logistics security platform.

Stage 2: Based on the characteristics of 5G wide connection and mass access, the main service scenario is mMTC, with specific applications including logistics intelligent energy supply, logistics intelligent warehousing, industrial-level logistics monitoring, and so on. As a transmission layer technology, 5G provides a powerful communication environment for intelligent storage, boosting the use of robots, shuttle vehicles, wearable devices, sorting devices, AGVs, etc., to improve operation efficiency and ensure operation safety.

Stage 3: Based on the characteristics of 5G with ultra-low delay, the main service scene is uRLLC, and the main service scene includes industrial-level vision system and fully automated logistics transportation. Among them, fully automated logistics transportation includes automatic driving of logistics trucks, formation driving of logistics fleets, unmanned aerial vehicle delivery system, and remote control of logistics nodes.

Stage 4: With the support of 5G slice technology, 5G enters the comprehensive promotion stage, and various business scenarios can be integrated into the integrated logistics system in the form of slice.

In transportation and distribution, the emergence of 5G can accelerate the application of automated transportation, unmanned driving, and other intelligent scenarios in the field of logistics, which can reduce the labor cost of transportation and distribution and improve transportation efficiency at the same time. In the storage link, 5G can realize intelligent storage management, efficient and intelligent sorting of goods to improve efficiency, and can also customize the storage environment for different goods to ensure the quality of goods. In the packaging and handling links, with the help of 5G, robots will be interconnected. The emergence of intelligent robots can greatly improve work efficiency and minimize the rate of cargo loss. As for logistics information, 5G's fast network can enable visual monitoring and real-time tracking of the entire operation process of logistics and realize efficient management of logistics information.

4.6 5G Helps Optimize the Upstream and Downstream Design of the Supply Chain

4.6.1 *Collaborative optimization design of upstream and downstream data of the supply chain based on 5G*

With the characteristics of low delay and high reliability, 5G will help break the situation of "information island" of enterprises, enable upstream and downstream suppliers to communicate with each other smoothly, and explore the network collaborative manufacturing mode with supply chain optimization as the core.

Product collaborative design based on 5G is based on digital design and manufacturing to build a production mode of collaboration of design, process, and manufacturing. Using AR/VR technology, all modules can be AR/VR equipment and eventually be combined to form the overall control of the entire equipment. The computer provides a powerful modeling and simulation environment, so that the parts of the product are simulated on the computer from the design to the process of production and assembly, optimization or system design, to carry on the optimization or the system design, and cause the product research and development the information to be fully shared throughout each link. The manufacturing of complex or high-end equipment requires the participation of many suppliers and final integration. The materials used and the strength of the material can be verified or simulated through the virtual prototype, which is of great help to the improvement of R&D efficiency and saving of R&D cost. Product collaborative design will change the traditional design and development mode, with the digital prototype as the core, the collaborative design of a single data source of parallel working mode must be realized, to ensure the uniqueness of the data in the design and manufacturing process.

4.6.2 *Typical application of 5G+ collaborative optimization design — semiconductor equipment*

The semiconductor industry has a complex industrial chain. From the upstream to the downstream, there are materials and equipment, chip design, chip manufacturing, and testing of chip products. The actual process of making chips, though different from material to material and process to process, generally uses similar processes, such as lithography and etching machines. Taking semiconductor etching equipment as an example, etching, as a semiconductor manufacturing process, is a very important step in the manufacturing process of microelectronic IC (Integrated Circuit) and micro-nano manufacturing process and is a major process of graphical processing associated with lithography. The design, development, production, and manufacturing of semiconductor etching equipment also involve a complex industrial chain. Therefore, cross-regional collaborative design of cloud-based semiconductor etching equipment, quality control of outsourcing processing process, intelligent production of product assembly and intelligent operation, and maintenance of product after-sales all put forward high requirements for the network.

A company builds a full life cycle platform for research and development, manufacturing, operation, and maintenance of global pan-semiconductor equipment based on 5G technology, builds an industrial Internet platform with 5G advanced technology as the core, and creates industrial-level application scenarios of pan-semiconductor industry with the help of 5G's features of high speed, low time delay, and wide connection. With the high speed characteristics of 5G, AR/VR-enabled semiconductor industry can use digital information to visualize, guide and improve the way to interact with physical devices, helping one to rebuild the service mode from product design, manufacturing to operation and maintenance.

In the 5G-based R&D, simulation collaboration of semiconductor equipment, this application adopts the transmission of data like 2D drawings, 3D models, and numerical analysis models collaboratively designed and simulatively output by reaction chamber of 5G network, automatic actuator, electrical system, gas system and other sub-modules, establishes a collaboration platform covering the industrial chain of chip designers, chip packers, chip testers, wafer processors, core equipment manufacturers, core module collaborators, key component manufacturers, and ODM/OEM manufacturers to improve the quality of product iteration and R&D efficiency, as shown in Fig. 4.20.

The Application of Intelligent Mass Production Based on 5G 117

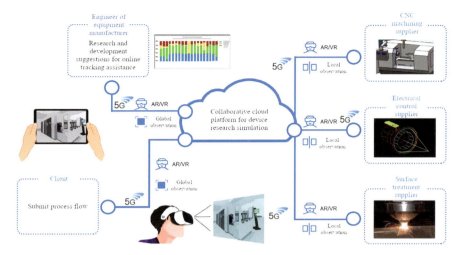

Figure 4.20 5G-based networked collaborative R&D architecture for semiconductor manufacturing equipment.

In terms of production and manufacturing collaboration in the semiconductor equipment industry based on 5G, the platform builds a process-level production collaboration platform, integrates seamlessly with the existing production system, and realizes intelligent production, networked collaboration, personalized customization, and service-oriented extension. Quality control is realized through 5G+ machine vision, and remote technical guidance for on-site workers is realized through AR technology to improve work efficiency.

As a catalyst, 5G technology has brought a comprehensive upgrade to all aspects of intelligent manufacturing. At the same time, the application of 5G+ intelligent manufacturing is still in the stage of exploration and preliminary application, and it will take some time to improve and promote comprehensively.

Conclusion

For the first time in human history, 5G wireless technology has broken the barrier between virtual and reality, shortened the distance between time and space, and closely connected the entire world physically and logically as a whole. It gives "intelligence" to every device and individual in the whole world through various intelligent and informationized means, making each individual more powerful. But, the tight connections between devices and individuals add enough complexity to the system. When the complexity of the whole system exceeds a limit, the quantitative change leads to qualitative change, and the whole socialized mass production system will become a complex symbiotic economy, with some characteristics that only organisms can have, and as a result, some new business models will be generated. Some imaginations that can only exist in science fiction or mythology can be presented in reality and create more social value.

5G+ intelligent manufacturing will turn society into a real organic life. Through the high speed, prevalence, and interconnection of the 5G wireless network technology, every aspect of human social life and production and everything can be connected through 5G wireless technology to access networks and connect to each intelligent node. These networks and intelligent nodes are like the nervous system, connecting the human society into an organic whole, realizing the physiological response, psychological response, and intelligent activity similar to the living body and becoming a more advanced life form that is detached from human beings.

120   *The World of 5G: Intelligent Manufacturing*

5G+ intelligent manufacturing will transform the industrial manufacturing mode into an agricultural ecological cultivation mode. The intelligent manufacturing system combined with 5G wireless technology will have a high degree of self-organization ability, rapid stress response ability, and flexible changeability. The smart factory will become an organ composed of production module cells. Like an organism, it will perceive the changes of the whole social production environment and constantly adjust itself to adapt to the whole social environment. The governance of industrial production in the future society will form a unified and perfect system, just like the "harmony between man and nature" in traditional Chinese culture, which spontaneously and quickly finds its optimal development mode in a similar way to ecological cultivation, influences the environment in the process of rapid adaptation to the environment, and creates a better world.

5G+ intelligent manufacturing will make people's real dreams come true and blur the boundary between virtual and reality. With the combination of 5G and virtual reality technology, the real world can be completely reflected in the virtual world of the computer network when the network bandwidth and computing power tend to be infinite. As intelligent manufacturing capabilities continue to increase, concepts in the virtual world can also be manufactured in the real-world in a faster and better way. All kinds of things that people imagine in the virtual world are likely to become real things in reality through intelligent manufacturing. With the latest virtual reality technology, human beings can experience the ultimate reality through their senses. Perhaps at that time, the philosophical speculation of Chuang Chou dreaming a butterfly will no longer be important. In the end, who you are will really depend on your self-perception.

5G+ intelligent manufacturing will divide the human race in two directions, namely, the organ type population with special function alienation and emphasis on cooperation and the strong and independent brain type population. The equipment will truly become the extension of human limbs. Since human beings no longer need to distinguish between the virtual and the real, the human consciousness is the core of being a person. The differentiation of consciousness is inevitable. Some people who are addicted to the flood of online information will become more influenced by the outside world. They may lose their independent consciousness and become subordinate consciousness nodes similar to organs. Only those people with strong will and firm belief can control the increasingly powerful information and with the assistance of the external brain become an

Conclusion 121

independent and powerful information processing core, influencing the development of the whole society.

5G+ intelligent manufacturing will blur the boundary between life and non-life. Due to the rapid development of 5G and intelligent manufacturing, artificial intelligence in the future will obtain stronger computing resources, massive learning data, and more optimized processing algorithms. Eventually, it will surpass a singularity of intelligence, similar to the Big Bang and lead to artificial intelligence having self-awareness. As the bandwidth of the connection increases, the human mind becomes more connected to the external devices and may see a device as part of itself. What is the essence of life at that time, the body or the mind?

5G+ intelligent manufacturing will greatly enhance people's imagination and creativity, so that everyone can become a creator. With the increasing impact of 5G and intelligent manufacturing on human production capacity and the reduction of human consciousness' dependence on the real world, humans' pursuit of material conditions will be greatly reduced, while the pursuit of the spiritual world will be more urgent. Therefore, unchanged and institutionalized products will no longer be attractive, and the wisdom crystallization of imagination and creativity will be the most valuable products in the future. People with creative ability will become the real creators, and talent and intelligence will become the most important resources in the future.

5G+ intelligent manufacturing will make the comparison between countries in the future become the comparison between systems. As 5G and smart manufacturing have built a society into an organic whole, the competition between countries in the future will not be military power, economic power, or political power, but all aspects of the whole system. In such a giant body connected by 5G communication technology and neural network, all the accumulated things of a country or region, including history, culture, social system, ideological crystallization, and human endowment, will be fully revealed in the ultra-high-dimensional connection of cyberspace. Therefore, in order to seize the opportunity in the competition between countries in the future world, we need to seize the opportunity in the current wave of 5G and intelligent manufacturing technology and move forward bravely.

Now, mankind has come to an unprecedented crossroads, at which we face both unprecedented opportunities and unprecedented challenges. With the development of technology, a small number of people can master the principle of technology, control the tide of technology, ride the wind and waves invincibly in the future, and become the leader of technology. With the development of technology, most people will enjoy the dividends of technology, promote the progress of technology, and become a solid foundation for future social progress. There are also some people who, due to various reasons, miss the tide of technological progress or resist the development of technology. They may eventually become the "relic of the old era", facing the risk of being eliminated by society.

5G and intelligent manufacturing are just the first wave of the current technology wave and also the foundation of future technology development. In such a wave of the arrival of the time, each of us should jump into this technology wave with an open mind and a positive attitude and strive to master the principle of technology and development trend. We should become a trendsetter in the new era and take the lead in the technological change of the new era.

Bibliography

China Hotel Association (August 26, 2019) [March 15, 2020]. 2019 Annual Report of China Catering Industry. https://www.vzkoo.com/doc/4562. html?a=4. CSDN (February 19, 2009) [March 31, 2020]. Selection of PLM system. https://blog.csdn.net/oscar999/article/details/3908519.

Fang Ruyi (2017). Key technology and analysis of 5G mobile communication network. *Information Technology* 1(1): 142–145.

Huawei (February 26, 2019) [March 15, 2020]. White paper on ten application scenarios in 5G era. https://www-file.huawei.com/-/media/corporate/pdf/mbb/5g-unlocks-a-world-of-opportunities-cn.PDF?La=zh&source=corp_comm.

Hu Jinquan (2017). Key technologies of 5G system and its development status at home and abroad. *China Telecom Express* 1(1): 10–14.

Industry Alliance of Industrial Internet (May 7, 2019) [March 15, 2020]. White paper on industrial Internet platform. http://www.miit.Gov.Cn/n973401/n5993937/n5993968/c6002326/content.html.

Liu Xu, Fei Qiang, Bai Yu *et al.* (2019). A review of super-dense networks. *Telecommunications Technology* 1(1): 18–20.

Ministry of Industry and Information Technology, Ministry of Finance (2016). Intelligent manufacturing development plan 2016–2020. http://www.miit.Gov.Cn/n1146295/n1652858/n1652930/n3757018/c5406111/content.html.

New Energy Vehicle Network (December 24, 2018) [March 31, 2020]. The intelligent ecological factory of GAC new energy has been formally completed. http://newenergy.automarket.net.cn/file/cyc/201812/3_3_1_61957_1.html.

Qianzhan Industrial Research Institute (November 28, 2019) [March 31, 2020]. Analysis of the Current Situation and Development Prospect of the Global Sensor Industry Market in 2019 Predicts that the Market Size will Exceed

124   *The World of 5G: Intelligent Manufacturing*

300 billion in 2024. https://bg.qianzhan.com/trends/detail/506/191128-4d16c3e8.html.

ROBODK Blog (January 11, 2018) [March 31, 2020]. What is the most effective way to program industrial robots? https://robodk.com/CN/blog/% e6% 9C%89% e6% 95%88% e6% 9C%BA% e5% 99% a8% e4% BA%BA% e7% BC%96% e7% a8% 8B/. S^2 Micro Salon (2017). *5G Enters the New Era of Internet of Everything.* Beijing: China Machine Press, p. 11.

SDNLAB (July 25, 2019) [March 31, 2020]. "Hot pot theory" of Network Slice: The same pot, different dreams. https://www.sdnlab.com/23417.html.

Sohu (October 11, 2018) [March 31, 2020]. The current situation and future of intelligent manufacturing!. http://www.sohu.com/a/258887285_99902166.

TechEconomy (October 2, 2018) [March 31, 2020]. All categories home devices experience double-digit growth. https://techeconomy.ng/2018/10/all-categories-of-smarthome-devices-experience-double-digit-growth-10494/.

Xiang Ligang (2019). *5G Era.* Beijing: Renmin University of China Press.

You Xiaohu, Pan Zhiwen, Gao Xiqi *et al.* (2014). 5G mobile communication development trend and several key technologies. *Science China (Information Science)* 44(5): 551–563.

Zhao Guofeng, Chen Jing, Han Yuanbing *et al.* (2015). Overview of key technologies of 5G mobile communication network. *Journal of Chongqing University of Posts and Telecommunications: Natural Science Edition* 27(4): 441–452.

Index

5G, v–vii, ix–xi, xiii–xv, 14, 18, 27, 31, 33–50, 58, 69–72, 78–80, 87–90, 92–93, 95–104, 106–117, 119–120

5G network, 36–41, 43, 45, 49–50, 71–72, 78–80, 97, 104, 108, 110–111, 114–117

A

artificial intelligence, v, ix–x, 4, 16, 20, 22, 24, 28, 34, 39, 42, 48, 60, 82–84, 88–89, 95–97, 102, 121

augmented reality (AR), 35, 39, 45–46, 69–73, 78–81, 96, 99–101, 103–104, 114–117

automated-guided vehicles (AGVs), 33, 39, 94

automation, 4–5, 16–17, 20, 31–32, 35, 47, 51, 54–55, 60–63, 87–88, 91, 105

B

Big Data, 4, 10, 14, 31, 33–34, 39, 42, 48, 55, 64, 73, 82, 91, 95–98, 102–104, 106, 112–113

C

China, v, vii, x, xiii, 6, 10–11, 15, 36, 44–46, 70, 72–73, 80, 98

D

data, ix, 16–17, 19, 20, 25, 27, 30–33, 36, 38–39, 41–48, 51–52, 54–60, 62–66, 68, 71, 73, 77–79, 81, 83, 89–90, 93, 95–98, 101–104, 106, 108, 110, 112–116, 121

F

flexible manufacturing, 25, 70, 91, 104–105, 107–109

flexible production line, 36, 92–93, 107

G

Germany, 4–6, 10–11, 15, 53, 82

I

industrial cloud platform, 42–43, 48, 54–61, 63–66, 68, 108

industrial flexible robots, 91–93

Industrial Revolution, v–vi, xiii, 1–6, 10, 13–14, 16, 34, 46, 48

126   *The World of 5G: Intelligent Manufacturing*

industrial robots, 78–79, 87–93, 95–98

Industrial Value Chain Initiative, 4, 8–10

Industry 4.0, 4–6, 11, 15, 73, 107

intelligent management, 25–26, 63, 90, 105–106

intelligent manufacturing, 4–6, 8–11, 13–40, 42, 44–51, 54, 61, 69, 73, 77, 81, 87–88, 101, 105–106, 109, 117, 119–122

Internet of Things (IoT), ix–x, 6, 10, 14, 20, 24, 33, 35–36, 42, 45, 49, 54–55, 58, 63, 65, 72–73, 79, 96, 102–106, 108

Internet technology, 13, 16

Internet+, 73

J

Japan, 4, 8, 10, 82

L

labor, 2–3, 11, 14, 17, 116

layer, 29–30, 36, 38–40, 47, 55, 63–64, 108, 113

M

Made in China 2025, 11, 15, 73

manufacturing enterprises, 17, 25, 30, 61, 67

manufac   ing industry, xiii, 6–8, 10–11   3–14, 16–18, 25, 32, 38, 42–44, 54–55, 72–73, 87–88, 99, 101, 110, 112

manufacturing innovation, xiv, 4, 6–8, 15

manufacturing USA, 7

P

production process optimization, 38, 63–64

R

reality/virtual reality, 69

remote maintenance, 36, 79–82

S

scenarios, 19, 22, 32–33, 35–36, 39–42, 45–46, 55, 62, 64–65, 67–70, 78, 80, 88, 96, 101, 112, 114–116

sensor, 16, 23, 27, 30–32, 38, 48–54, 62, 64, 68, 72, 82, 94–97, 103–104

supply chain, 31, 51, 63, 65–66, 106, 110, 112–115

U

United States, x, 6–7, 10, 15